The Forty Thieves

The Marvel of the Sword

Pies of the Princess

Three Fridays

Paul Goes Hunting

The Hungry Old Witch

The Voyage of the Wee Red Cap

The Huckabuck Family and How They Raised Pop Corn

Robinson Crusoe's Story

The River B

Aladdin and the Wonderful Lamp

The Travels of Baron Munchausen

The Doughnuts

D0359828

Through Golden Windows

THROUGH GOLDEN WINDOWS

Edited by

Nora Beust, M.A.

Phyllis Fenner, B.A., B.L.S.

Bernice E. Leary, PH.D.

Mary Katharine Reely, B.A.

Dora V. Smith, PH.D.

Editor-in-Chief
Jeanne Hale, B.A.
Assistant Editor
Muriel Johnstone, B.A.

Fun and Fantasy

Grolier

INCORPORATED

NEW YORK

Acknowledgments
and Copyright Notice

Through Golden Windows

IN A reading world filled with children's books the addition of one more anthology or set of anthologies leads naturally to the question "Why?" We, who compiled *Through Golden Windows,* first asked ourselves that question almost ten years ago. We are still asking it. Always we arrive at the same answer. "The books are needed."

The power of books has long been recognized. And never more than today when material things are assuming increasing importance, and even the simple act of opening a door is fast getting out of human hands; when global and continental distances are shrinking from weeks and days to hours and minutes, and nearness at home means crowded living, crowded schools and playgrounds, crowded streets and highways; when family ties are weakening and children suffer from want of close, two-parent affection and guidance.

What can books give to a child who is growing up in today's curiously complicated world? Many things, we believe, although the evidence is not altogether conclusive. Facts and information, of course, about almost everything; understanding of himself and others; confidence and security; fun and laughter; friends and friendships; escape from reality at times, and again the courage to face reality—all these are possible results if the right book is used with the right child in the right way.

But suppose the right book is not available? Crowded living means limited space for books, at home and at school. Or suppose parents and teachers do not know the right book? Many, by their own admission, do not know children's books well. Must the child's values in reading be left to chance, while he struggles with his everyday problems, or grows up without feeling the full rapture of a good book?

Through Golden Windows grew out of a fear, on the one hand, that children's needs are not being met well enough through books; and out of a faith, on the other hand, that carefully compiled anthologies, easily accessible, would help teachers and parents do a better job of guiding children's reading.

Such books, we believe, should give children experience—here, there and everywhere. It should give them variety—sober fact and gay fantasy, practical prose and picture-filled poetry, lives of the great and the everyday intimacy of home folks, history of the past and history in the making, high adventure and the small thrills of daily living. It should show them some of the wonders of the earth and sky and the great achievements of great men. It should assure them the safe moorings of home and country, of family and friends. It should give them confidence in themselves and in others, and in a world that, for all its problems, is a wonderful world to grow up in.

To be most useful, each book should be not too large and not too small, not too easy and not too difficult, but "just right" for the child in pre-school and primary grades or in middle and upper grades. Based on children's interests and reading preferences, it should have not too much nor too little of any one type of material, but a balanced content that would invite all readers.

Through Golden Windows, therefore, was made with an eye on the child and his needs and interests at different stages of development. Bound in ten volumes, each book is attractive to look at, comfortable to hold, interesting to read, and easy to talk about.

Taken together, these books represent five large areas of interest: fun and humor, adventure, children everywhere, the story of America, and science. For each area there are two volumes, one for children of pre-school and primary age, and the other for intermediate grade readers. Hence, as a child grows in reading power, he may move from *Mostly Magic* to *Fun and Fantasy,* and satisfy his need for fun in both. Again, for adventure he may enjoy *Wonderful Things Happen* until he is ready for *Adventures Here and There.* His broadening interest in people finds satisfaction first in *Good Times Together* and later in *Children Everywhere.* Similarly, *Stories of Early America* eventually gives way to *American Backgrounds* and *Wide, Wonderful World* to *Man and His World.*

Within each volume, the selections are loosely tied together into related units, in order that a child may pursue an interest in Pets or Pioneers or Plants, for example, without searching for "more." The obvious overlapping of units and of volumes is not without purpose or benefit. Were it possible to organize reading materials into airtight, dark little compartments, *Through Golden Windows* would defeat its purpose to help "the whole child" to live and grow. On the other hand, a free, less exacting organization allows him to find the same inter-relationships and similarities among his reading experiences as exist in his daily life.

Through Golden Windows, then, aims first to satisfy the child, meet his everyday needs and help him find early the absorbing joy of reading. It aims, also, to acquaint teachers with much of the best in children's books. Used as basic reading in a college course in children's literature, *Through Golden Windows* will help to overcome the limitations imposed by a barren reading childhood and give teachers and parents that first security they need to guide children's reading. Beyond such a course lies a whole world of books that teachers will continue to explore, year after year.

It aims, finally, to help parents by providing a basic home library for their children. Here are stories as old as "Once upon a time" and as new as the children themselves. Here are stories and poems to read aloud and to read to one's self in a quiet corner, "to-go-to-sleep-by" and "to-get-up-with," to laugh at and to learn from, to sing and to act, and sometimes to read for no other reason than the fun of doing something together as a family.

It is to children, teachers, and parents everywhere that these books are affectionately dedicated, in the hope that through the pages they may see, as "through golden windows," the rewarding vista of life itself.

BERNICE E. LEARY

viii

Fun and Fantasy

I WAS going through a door with an electric eye in a large railway station. Behind me was a gang of boys. As they rushed through the opening door one of them whooped, "Open sesame." I remember feeling a peculiar pleasure hearing these words, thinking that the boys were acquainted with something from *The Arabian Nights*. Knowing the old tales is like knowing a common language. We say "He is a Galahad," or, "She was a Cinderella." Again, "Don't kill the goose that laid the golden egg." When someone wants us to do his dirty work we say "I won't be your man Friday." A wandering is called "an Odyssey." A liar is spoken of as "a Munchausen." These expressions mean something to people of all languages because they come from those old tales that are known the world over.

Some of these old tales we call "fairy tales." Yet, we don't necessarily mean stories of "the little people." The word "fairy" comes from a word meaning "to enchant," to be carried off to another world, away from this humdrum place we know. Most of these tales are not just "fairy tales." They are "folk tales" which have been handed down for generations. They have roots. They give a child security in his literary past. They are a bit of magical adventure, a touch of humor, a lot of fun, especially when shared. Most of them will seem like "old stuff" to us grownups, but as the book clerk said to the customer, who complained that he was showing her old books, "But Madame, the children are new."

What a wonderful opportunity we have to share something we have loved with children. And don't forget. Children will understand the magic better than we do. They know what giants and trolls are. Many of us forgot long ago.

PHYLLIS FENNER

Contents

xii

M ANY years ago there lived an Emperor who was so exceedingly fond of fine new clothes that he spent all his money on being elaborately dressed. He took no interest in his soldiers, no interest in the theater, nor did he care to drive about in his state coach, unless it were to show off his new clothes. He had different robes for every hour of the day, and just as one says of a King that he is in his Council Chamber, people always said of him, "The Emperor is in his wardrobe!"

The great city in which he lived was full of gaiety. Strangers were always coming and going. One day two swindlers arrived; they made themselves out to be weavers, and said they knew how to weave the most magnificent fabric that one could imagine. Not only were the colors and patterns unusually beautiful, but the clothes that were made of this material had the extraordinary quality of becoming invisible to everyone who was either unfit for his post, or inexcusably stupid.

The Emperor's New Clothes

BY HANS CHRISTIAN ANDERSEN

Illustrated by Fritz Kredel

"What useful clothes to have!" thought the Emperor. "If I had some like that, I might find out which of the people in my Empire are unfit for their posts. I should also be able to distinguish the wise from the fools. Yes, that material must be woven for me immediately!" Then he gave the swindlers large sums of money so that they could start work at once.

Quickly they set up two looms and pretended to weave, but there was not a trace of anything on the frames. They

1

made no bones about demanding the finest silk and the purest gold thread. They stuffed everything into their bags, and continued to work at the empty looms until late into the night.

"I'm rather anxious to know how much of the material is finished," thought the Emperor, but to tell the truth, he felt a bit uneasy, remembering that anyone who was either a fool or unfit for his post would never be able to see it. He rather imagined that he need not have any fear for himself, yet he thought it wise to send someone else first to see how things were going. Everyone in the town knew about the exceptional powers of the material, and all were eager to know how incompetent or how stupid their neighbors might be.

"I will send my honest old Chamberlain to the weavers," thought the Emperor. "He will be able to judge the fabric better than anyone else, for he has brains, and nobody fills his post better than he does."

So the nice old Chamberlain went into the hall where the two swindlers were sitting working at the empty looms.

"Upon my life!" he thought, opening his eyes very wide, "I can't see anything at all!" But he didn't say so.

Both the swindlers begged him to be good enough to come nearer, and asked how he liked the unusual design and the splendid colors. They pointed to the empty looms, and the poor old Chamberlain opened his eyes wider and wider, but he could see nothing, for there was nothing. "Heavens above!" he thought, "could it possibly be that I am stupid? I have never thought that of myself, and not a soul must know it. Could it be that I am not fit for my post? It will never do for me to admit that I can't see the material!"

"Well, you don't say what you think of it," said one of the weavers.

2

"Oh, it's delightful—most exquisite!" said the old Chamberlain, looking through his spectacles. "What a wonderful design and what beautiful colors! I shall certainly tell the Emperor that I am enchanted with it."

"We're very pleased to hear that," said the two weavers, and they started describing the colors and the curious pattern. The old Chamberlain listened carefully in order to repeat, when he came home to the Emperor, exactly what he had heard, and he did so.

The swindlers now demanded more money, as well as more silk and gold thread, saying that they needed it for weaving. They put everything into their pockets and not a thread appeared upon the looms, but they kept on working at the empty frames as before.

Soon after this, the Emperor sent another nice official to see how the weaving was getting on, and to enquire whether the stuff would soon be ready. Exactly the same thing happened to him as to the Chamberlain. He looked and looked, but as there was nothing to be seen except the empty looms, he could see nothing.

"Isn't it a beautiful piece of material?" said the swindlers, showing and describing the pattern that did not exist at all.

"Stupid I certainly am not," thought the official; "then I must be unfit for my excellent post, I suppose. That seems rather funny—but I'll take great care that nobody gets wind of it." Then he praised the material he could not see, and assured them of his enthusiasm for the gorgeous colors and the beautiful pattern. "It's simply enchanting!" he said to the Emperor.

The whole town was talking about the splendid material.

And now the Emperor was curious to see it for himself while it was still upon the looms.

3

Accompanied by a great number of selected people, among whom were the two nice old officials who had already been there, the Emperor went forth to visit the two wily swindlers. They were now weaving madly, yet without a single thread upon the looms.

"Isn't it magnificent?" said the two nice officials. "Will Your Imperial Majesty deign to look at this splendid pattern and these glorious colors?" Then they pointed to the empty looms, for each thought that the others could probably see the material.

"What on earth can this mean?" thought the Emperor. "I don't see anything! This is terrible. Am I stupid? Am I unfit to be Emperor? That would be the most disastrous thing that could possibly befall me. Oh, it's perfectly wonderful!" he said. "It quite meets with my Imperial approval." And he nodded appreciatively and stared at the empty looms—he would not admit that he saw nothing. His whole suite looked and looked, but with as little result as the others; nevertheless, they all said, like the Emperor, "It's perfectly wonderful!" They advised him to have some new clothes made from this splendid stuff and to wear them for the first time in the next great procession.

4

"Magnificent!" "Excellent!" "Prodigious!" went from mouth to mouth, and everyone was exceedingly pleased. The Emperor gave each of the swindlers a decoration to wear in his button-hole, and the title of "Knight of the Loom."

Before the procession they worked all night, burning more than sixteen candles. People could see how busy they were finishing the Emperor's new clothes. They pretended to take the material from the looms, they slashed the air with great scissors, they sewed with needles without any thread, and finally they said, "The Emperor's clothes are ready!"

Then the Emperor himself arrived with his most distinguished courtiers, and each swindler raised an arm as if he were holding something, and said, "These are Your Imperial Majesty's knee-breeches. This is Your Imperial Majesty's robe. This is Your Imperial Majesty's mantle," and so forth. "It is all as light as a spider's web, one might fancy one had nothing on, but that is just the beauty of it!"

"Yes, indeed," said all the courtiers, but they could see nothing, for there was nothing to be seen.

"If Your Imperial Majesty would graciously consent to take off your clothes," said the swindlers, "we could fit on the new ones in front of the long glass."

So the Emperor laid aside his clothes, and the swindlers pretended to hand him, piece by piece, the new ones they were supposed to have made, and they fitted him round the waist, and acted as if they were fastening something on—it was the train; and the Emperor turned round and round in front of the long glass.

"How well the new robes suit Your Imperial Majesty! How well they fit!" they all said. "What a splendid design! What gorgeous colors! It's all magnificently regal!"

"The canopy which is to be held over Your Imperial Maj-

esty in the procession is waiting outside," announced the Lord High Chamberlain.

"Well, I suppose I'm ready," said the Emperor. "Don't you think they are a nice fit?" And he looked at himself again in the glass, first on one side and then the other, as if he really were carefully examining his handsome attire.

The courtiers who were to carry the train groped about on the floor with fumbling fingers, and pretended to lift it; they walked on, holding their hands up in the air; nothing would have induced them to admit that they could not see anything.

And so the Emperor set off in the procession under the beautiful canopy, and everybody in the streets and at the windows said, "Oh! how superb the Emperor's new clothes are! What a gorgeous train! What a perfect fit!" No one would acknowledge that he didn't see anything, so proving

6

that he was not fit for his post, or that he was very stupid.

None of the Emperor's clothes had ever met with such a success. "But he hasn't any clothes on!" gasped out a little child.

"Good heavens! Hark at the little innocent!" said the father, and people whispered to one another what the child had said. "But he hasn't any clothes on! There's a little child saying he hasn't any clothes on!"

"But he hasn't any clothes on!" shouted the whole town at last. The Emperor had a creepy feeling down his spine, because it began to dawn upon him that the people were right. "All the same," he thought to himself, "I've got to go through with it as long as the procession lasts."

So he drew himself up and held his head higher than before, and the courtiers held on to the train that wasn't there at all.

HO, for the Pirate Don Durk of Dowdee!
He was as wicked as wicked could be,
But oh, he was perfectly gorgeous to see!
The Pirate Don Durk of Dowdee.

His conscience, of course, was as black as a bat,
But he had a floppety plume on his hat
And when he went walking it jiggled—like that!
The plume of the Pirate Dowdee.

His coat it was crimson and
cut with a slash,
And often as ever he twirled
his mustache
Deep down in the ocean the
mermaids went splash,
Because of Don
Durk of Dowdee.

Pirate Don Durk of Dowdee

BY

MILDRED PLEW MEIGS

Illustrated by Roger Duvoisin

Moreover, Dowdee had a
purple tattoo,
And stuck in his belt where
he buckled it through
Were a dagger, a dirk and a squizzamaroo,
For fierce was the Pirate Dowdee.

So fearful he was he would shoot at a puff,
And always at sea when the weather grew rough
He drank from a bottle and wrote on his cuff,
Did Pirate Don Durk of Dowdee.

Oh, he had a cutlass that swung at his thigh
And he had a parrot called Pepperkin Pye,
And a zigzaggy scar at the end of his eye
   Had Pirate Don Durk of Dowdee.

He kept in a cavern, this buccaneer bold,
A curious chest that was covered with mould,
And all of his pockets were jingly with gold!
   Oh jing! went the gold of Dowdee.

His conscience, of course, it was crook'd like a squash,
But both of his boots made a slickery slosh,
And he went through the world with a wonderful swash,
   Did Pirate Don Durk of Dowdee.

It's true he was wicked as wicked could be,
His sins they outnumbered a hundred and three,
But oh, he was perfectly gorgeous to see,
   The Pirate Don Durk of Dowdee.

ONCE upon a time, in a kingdom by the sea, there lived a little Princess named Lenore. She was ten years old, going on eleven. One day Lenore fell ill of a surfeit of raspberry tarts and took to her bed.

The Royal Physician came to see her and took her temperature and felt her pulse and made her stick out her tongue.

The Royal Physician was worried. He sent for the King, Lenore's father, and the King came to see her.

"I will get you anything your heart desires," the King said. "Is there anything your heart desires?"

"Yes," said the Princess. "I want the moon. If I can have the moon, I will be well again."

Now the King had a great many wise men who always got for him anything he wanted, so he told his daughter that she could have the moon. Then he went to the throne room and

Many Moons

BY JAMES THURBER

Illustrated by Louis Slobodkin

pulled a bell cord, three long pulls and a short pull, and presently the Lord High Chamberlain came into the room.

The Lord High Chamberlain was a large, fat man who wore thick glasses which made his eyes seem twice as big as they really were. This made the Lord High Chamberlain seem twice as wise as he really was.

"I want you to get the moon," said the King. "The Princess Lenore wants the moon. If she can have the moon, she will get well again."

"The moon?" exclaimed the Lord High Chamberlain, his eyes widening. This made him look four times as wise as he really was.

10

"Yes, the moon," said the King. "M-o-o-n, moon. Get it tonight, tomorrow at the latest!"

The Lord High Chamberlain wiped his forehead with a handkerchief and then blew his nose loudly. "I have got a great many things for you in my time, your Majesty," he said. "It just happens that I have with me a list of the things I have got for you in my time." He pulled a long scroll of parchment out of his pocket. "Let me see, now." He glanced at the list, frowning. "I have got ivory, apes, and peacocks, rubies, opals, and emeralds, black orchids, pink elephants, and blue poodles, gold bugs, scarabs, and flies in amber, humming-birds' tongues, angels' feathers, and unicorns' horns, giants, midgets, and mermaids, frankincense, ambergris, and myrrh, troubadors, minstrels, and dancing women, a pound of butter, two dozen eggs, and a sack of sugar—sorry, my wife wrote that in there."

"I don't remember any blue poodles," said the King.

"It says blue poodles right here on the list, and they are checked off with a little check mark," said the Lord High Chamberlain. "So there must have been blue poodles. You just forget."

"Never mind the blue poodles," said the King. "What I want now is the moon."

"I have sent as far as Samarkand and Araby and Zanzibar to get things for you, your Majesty," said the Lord High Chamberlain. "But the moon is out of the question. It is 35,000 miles away and it is bigger than the room the Princess lies in. Furthermore, it is made of molten copper. I cannot get the moon for you. Blue poodles, yes; the moon, no."

The King flew into a rage and told the Lord High Chamberlain to leave the room and to send the Royal Wizard to the throne room.

11

The Royal Wizard was a little, thin man with a long face. He wore a high red peaked hat covered with silver stars, and a long blue robe covered with golden owls. His face grew very pale when the King told him that he wanted the moon for his little daughter, and that he expected the Royal Wizard to get it.

"I have worked a great deal of magic for you in my time, your Majesty," said the Royal Wizard. "As a matter of fact, I just happen to have in my pocket a list of the wizardries I have performed for you." He drew a paper from a deep pocket of his robe. "It begins: 'Dear Royal Wizard: I am returning herewith the so-called philosopher's stone which you claimed—' no, that isn't it." The Royal Wizard brought a long scroll of parchment from another pocket of his robe. "Here it is," he said. "Now, let's see. I have squeezed blood out of turnips for you, and turnips out of blood. I have produced rabbits out of silk hats, and silk hats out of rabbits. I have conjured up flowers, tambourines, and doves out of nowhere, and nowhere out of flowers, tambourines and doves. I have brought you divining rods, magic wands, and crystal spheres in which to behold the future. I have compounded philters, unguents, and potions to cure heartbreak, surfeit, and ringing in the ears. I have made you my own special mixture of wolfbane, nightshade, and eagles' tears to ward off witches, demons, and things that go bump in the night. I have given you seven league boots, the golden touch, and a cloak of invisibility—"

"It didn't work," said the King. "The cloak of invisibility didn't work."

"Yes, it did," said the Royal Wizard.

"No, it didn't," said the King. "I kept bumping into things, the same as ever."

12

"The cloak is supposed to make you invisible," said the Royal Wizard. "It is not supposed to keep you from bumping into things."

"All I know is, I kept bumping into things," said the King.

The Royal Wizard looked at his list again. "I got you," he said, "horns from Elfland, sand from the Sandman, and gold from the rainbow. Also a spool of thread, a paper of needles, and a lump of beeswax—sorry, those are things my wife wrote down for me to get her."

"What I want you to do now," said the King, "is to get me the moon. The Princess Lenore wants the moon, and when she gets it, she will be well again."

"Nobody can get the moon," said the Royal Wizard. "It is 150,000 miles away, and it is made of green cheese, and it is twice as big as this palace."

The King flew into another rage and sent the Royal Wizard back to his cave. Then he rang a gong and summoned the Royal Mathematician.

The Royal Mathematician was a bald-headed, near-sighted man, with a skullcap on his head and a pencil behind each ear. He wore a black suit with white numbers on it.

"I don't want to hear a long list of all the

things you have figured out for me since 1907," the King said to him. "I want you to figure out right now how to get the moon for the Princess Lenore. When she gets the moon, she will be well again."

"I am glad you mentioned all the things I have figured out for you since 1907," said the Royal Mathematician. "It so happens that I have a list of them with me."

He pulled a long scroll of parchment out of a pocket and looked at it. "Now let me see. I have figured out for you the distance between the horns of a dilemma, night and day, and A and Z. I have computed how far is Up, how long it takes to get to Away, and what becomes of Gone. I have discovered the length of the sea serpent, the price of the priceless, and the square of the hippopotamus. I know where you are when you are at Sixes and Sevens, how much Is you have to have to make an Are, and how many birds you can catch with the salt in the ocean—187,796,132, if it would interest you to know."

"There aren't that many birds," said the King.

"I didn't say there were," said the Royal Mathematician. "I said if there were."

"I don't want to hear about seven hundred million imaginary birds," said the King. "I want you to get the moon for the Princess Lenore."

"The moon is 300,000 miles away," said the Royal Mathematician. "It is round and flat like a coin, only it is made of asbestos, and it is half the size of this kingdom. Furthermore, it is pasted on the sky. Nobody can get the moon."

The King flew into still another rage and sent the Royal Mathematician away. Then he rang for the Court Jester. The Jester came bounding into the throne room in his motley and his cap and bells, and sat at the foot of the throne.

14

"What can I do for you, your Majesty?" asked the Court Jester.

"Nobody can do anything for me," said the King mournfully. "The Princess Lenore wants the moon, and she cannot be well till she gets it, but nobody can get it for her. Every time I ask anybody for the moon, it gets larger and farther away. There is nothing you can do for me except play on your lute. Something sad."

"How big do they say the moon is," asked the Court Jester, "and how far away?"

"The Lord High Chamberlain says it is 35,000 miles away, and bigger than the Princess Lenore's room," said the King. "The Royal Wizard says it is 150,000 miles away, and twice as big as this palace. The Royal Mathematician says it is 300,000 miles away, and half the size of this kingdom."

The Court Jester strummed on his lute for a little while. "They are all wise men," he said, "and so they must all be right. If they are all right, then the moon must be just as large and as far away as each person thinks it is. The thing to do is find out how big the Princess Lenore thinks it is, and how far away."

"I never thought of that," said the King.

"I will go and ask her, your Majesty," said the Court Jester. And he crept softly into the little girl's room.

The Princess Lenore was awake, and she was glad to see the Court Jester, but her face was very pale and her voice very weak.

"Have you brought the moon to me?" she asked.

"Not yet," said the Court Jester, "but I will get it for you right away. How big do you think it is?"

"It is just a little smaller than my thumbnail," she said,

15

"for when I hold my thumbnail up at the moon, it just covers it."

"And how far away is it?" asked the Court Jester.

"It is not as high as the big tree outside my window," said the Princess, "for sometimes it gets caught in the top branches."

"It will be very easy to get the moon for you," said the Court Jester. "I will climb the tree tonight when it gets caught in the top branches and bring it to you."

Then he thought of something else. "What is the moon made of, Princess?" he asked.

"Oh," she said, "it's made of gold, of course, silly."

The Court Jester left the Princess Lenore's room and went to see the Royal Goldsmith. He had the Royal Goldsmith make a tiny round golden moon just a little smaller than the thumbnail of the Princess Lenore. Then he had him string it on a golden chain so the Princess could wear it around her neck.

"What is this thing I have made?" asked the Royal Goldsmith when he had finished it.

"You have made the moon," said the Court Jester. "That is the moon."

"But the moon," said the Royal Goldsmith, "is 500,000 miles away and is made of bronze and is round like a marble."

"That's what you think," said the Court Jester as he went away with the moon.

The Court Jester took the moon to the Princess Lenore, and she was overjoyed. The next day she was well again and could get up and go out in the gardens to play.

But the King's worries were not yet over. He knew that the moon would shine in the sky again that night, and he did not want the Princess Lenore to see it. If she did, she would know that the moon she wore on a chain around her neck was not the real moon.

So the King sent for the Lord High Chamberlain and said, "We must keep the Princess Lenore from seeing the moon when it shines in the sky tonight. Think of something."

The Lord High Chamberlain tapped his forehead with his fingers thoughtfully and said, "I know just the thing. We can make some dark glasses for the Princess Lenore. We can make them so dark that she will not be able to see anything at all through them. Then she will not be able to see the moon when it shines in the sky."

This made the King very angry, and he shook his head from side to side. "If she wore dark glasses, she would bump into things," he said, "and then she would be ill again." So he sent the Lord High Chamberlain away and called the Royal Wizard.

"We must hide the moon," said the King, "so that the Princess Lenore will not see it when it shines in the sky tonight. How are we going to do that?"

The Royal Wizard stood on his hands and then he stood on his head and then he stood on his feet again. "I know what we can do," he said. "We can stretch some black velvet curtains on poles. The curtains will cover all the palace gardens like a circus tent, and the Princess Lenore will not be able to see through them, so she will not see the moon in the sky."

The King was so angry at this that he waved his arms around. "Black velvet curtains would keep out the air," he said. "The Princess Lenore would not be able to breathe, and she would be ill again." So he sent the Royal Wizard away and summoned the Royal Mathematician.

"We must do something," said the King, "so that the Princess Lenore will not see the moon when it shines in the sky tonight. If you know so much, figure out a way to do that."

The Royal Mathematician walked around in a circle, and then he walked around in a square, and then he stood still. "I have it!" he said. "We can set off fireworks in the gardens every night. We will make a lot of silver fountains and golden cascades, and when they go off, they will fill the sky with so many sparks that it will be as light as day and the Princess Lenore will not be able to see the moon."

The King flew into such a rage that he began jumping up and down. "Fireworks would keep the Princess Lenore awake," he said. "She would not get any sleep at all and she would be ill again." So the King sent the Royal Mathematician away.

When he looked up again, it was dark outside and he saw the bright rim of the moon just peeping over the horizon. He jumped up in a great fright and rang for the Court Jester. The Court Jester came bounding into the room and sat down at the foot of the throne.

"What can I do for you, your Majesty?" he asked.

"Nobody can do anything for me," said the King, mournfully. "The moon is coming up again. It will shine into the Princess Lenore's bedroom, and she will know it is still in the sky and that she does not wear it on a golden chain around her neck. Play me something on your lute, something very sad, for when the Princess sees the moon, she will be ill again."

The Court Jester strummed on his lute. "What do your wise men say?" he asked.

"They can think of no way to hide the moon that will not make the Princess Lenore ill," said the King.

The Court Jester played another song, very softly. "Your wise men know everything," he said, "and if they cannot hide the moon, then it cannot be hidden."

The King put his head in his hands again and sighed. Suddenly he jumped up from his throne and pointed to the windows. "Look!" he cried. "The moon is already shining into the Princess Lenore's bedroom. Who can explain how the moon can be shining in the sky when it is hanging on a golden chain around her neck?"

The Court Jester stopped playing on his lute. "Who could explain how to get the moon when your wise men said it was too large and too far away? It was the Princess Lenore. Therefore the Princess Lenore is wiser than your wise men and knows more about the moon than they do. So I will ask

19

her." And before the King could stop him, the Court Jester slipped quietly out of the throne room and up the wide marble staircase to the Princess Lenore's bedroom.

The Princess was lying in bed, but she was wide awake and she was looking out the window at the moon shining in the sky. Shining in her hand was the moon the Court Jester had got for her. He looked very sad, and there seemed to be tears in his eyes. "Tell me, Princess Lenore," he said mournfully, "how can the moon be shining in the sky when it is hanging on a golden chain around your neck?"

The Princess looked at him and laughed. "That is easy, silly," she said. "When I lose a tooth, a new one grows in its place, doesn't it?"

"Of course," said the Court Jester. "And when the unicorn loses his horn in the forest, a new one grows in the middle of his forehead."

"That is right," said the Princess. "And when the Royal Gardener cuts the flowers in the garden, other flowers come to take their place."

"I should have thought of that," said the Court Jester, "for it is the same way with the daylight."

"And it is the same way with the moon," said the Princess Lenore. "I guess it is the same way with everything." Her voice became very low and faded away, and the Court Jester saw that she was asleep. Gently he tucked the covers in around the sleeping Princess.

But before he left the room, he went over to the window and winked at the moon, for it seemed to the Court Jester that the moon had winked at him.

20

OF ALL the storekeepers in town there are none so merry as Mr. A and Mr. P.

They have quite the grandest store on the street. Outside it is painted a bright cheerful red, and inside it is full of all the things that a grocery store should have—soap and crackers and sardines and tubs of butter and red shiny apples, besides shelves and shelves of everything you could possibly think of, all put up in cans.

Mr. A is tall and thin, and Mr. P is short and stout. Mr. A has red hair, and Mr. P has very little hair at all. Mr. A can reach all the things off the top shelves, and Mr. P can get all the things off the bottom shelves. If there is anything on the very top shelf of all, and they have to get the long poker and poke it down, then Mr. A pokes and Mr. P catches, because Mr. P's lap is the widest.

Mr. A and Mr. P

BY MARGERY BIANCO

Illustrated by Grace Paull

In fact they do everything together. Mr. A takes the money and Mr. P rings the bell. Mr. A counts the groceries, and Mr. P writes them down. Mr. A makes the jokes, and Mr. P laughs at them.

And of an evening, when the store is closed and work is over, then Mr. A plays the flute and Mr. P plays the accordion.

You would think that when two people get along together so well, they would never have a quarrel in the world. But once upon a time they did, and this is how it happened.

For a long time they had been wondering what to do to make their life even merrier than it was. They had tried play-

21

ing baseball with the soup cans, and football with the watermelons, and building all sorts of castles out of ketchup bottles and breakfast foods, just to see them come tumbling down again. But after a while they got tired of all this, and there just didn't seem anything new to play at.

Then Mr. A had a grand idea. He thought he would change the prices of everything in the store, over-night, just to see how surprised the customers would look when they came around next morning. He didn't want Mr. P to know about it, so that it might be a nice surprise for him, too. For Mr. A was always trying to think of something that would please Mr. P.

But Mr. P, too, was always trying to think of something that would please and surprise Mr. A. And unfortunately he happened to think of exactly the same thing, and he thought of it at almost exactly the same moment as Mr. A.

So each of them, very secretly, set about writing a whole set of new tickets, and each of them, also very secretly, went about sticking the new tickets just where they thought it would be most fun.

Mr. A would turn his head suddenly and want to know what Mr. P was giggling about, and Mr. P would stop writing his secret tickets long enough to ask why Mr. A was chuckling so, and they would both go off into peals of laughter and then look very solemn and begin working away again faster than ever.

Finally they locked up their store and went home for the night.

The first customer to come next morning was a housewife, and she wanted three cakes of soap for a quarter.

"Twelve cents a-piece!" said Mr. A, for he had changed the tickets from the breakfast cereal.

"But they're always three for a quarter," said the house-wife.

"Not now, not now!" said Mr. A. "Maybe you're thinking of soup. Soup's three for a quarter. To-day," he added, and then began to giggle. He couldn't help it.

"Why, no it isn't!" cried Mr. P, beginning to giggle too. "It's two for nineteen. Look at that!"

And he winked at Mr. A, but for some reason Mr. A didn't seem to think it was funny at all.

"I tell you it's three for a quarter!" he said indignantly. "The whole week, too!"

"Two for nineteen, two for nineteen!" chanted Mr. P, in an irritating sort of way, and he went about the store humming. "Two for nineteen, two for nineteen!"

"Just like a hen that's laid an egg!" thought Mr. A, beginning to get very annoyed, as people do when their jokes don't turn out to be funny after all.

The next customer wanted sugar and potatoes.

"Six for fifteen!" shouted Mr. P loudly.

"Two for forty-nine!" yelled Mr. A, banging his fist on the counter.

The customers began to get worried. They didn't know

what to make of it at all. And the more Mr. A chuckled, the madder Mr. P got, and every time Mr. P giggled, Mr. A was cross enough to bite his head off.

In the afternoon it was worse. No one knew what anything cost at all. Half the customers were buying all sorts of things they didn't need just because they were cheap, and the other half were shouting that they wanted their money back. As fast as Mr. A stuck a ticket on one shelf Mr. P tore it down and put a different one in its place. They kept rushing round and round the store, doing nothing but change the tickets, and the last straw was when Mr. A marked a whole crate of water-melons four for fifteen cents, and all the boys from the neighborhood came pouring into the store so fast one couldn't even count them. And above all the turmoil, and the customers snatching this thing and that—for by this time they were so confused that they started waiting on one another—you might hear Mr. A's high squeaky voice shouting "Six for nine-teen! Six for nineteen, I tell you!" and Mr. P's deep bass rumbling "Three for a quarter! Three for a quarter!"

It was like a nightmare!

When six o'clock came round Mr. A and Mr. P were both exhausted. Mr. A just threw his apron over his head and started rushing off down the street on his long thin legs, look-ing neither to right nor left, while Mr. P shooed the last cus-tomer out of the store and then sank right down on the onion crate and burst out sobbing.

He sobbed for quite a long time. When he had finished he felt a little bit better. So he mopped his eyes and blew his nose, and then he jumped up off the onion crate and rushed out of the store, not even banging the door behind him, and pat-tered off along the sidewalk as fast as he could go.

It was the very first time in all their lives that Mr. A and

Mr. P had not walked home together. For years they had hung their two little aprons up side by side at exactly six o'clock, and at exactly two minutes past six they had taken their two hats and locked the store and strolled home side by side.

But this time Mr. A hadn't even gone home at all. He was far too upset. He went striding along through the town very fast, not caring at all which way he went, till he came to the place where the sidewalk ended and the country began, and there Mr. P finally saw him, still striding along with his nose in the air and his apron flapping in the breeze.

Now Mr. A was walking much faster than Mr. P, and so Mr. P had to make his stout little legs work very hard indeed to catch up with him, but catch up he did. And as soon as Mr. A heard that little patter-patter coming along behind him he slowed down a bit, and pretended to be looking at the landscape. So side by side, but neither looking at the other, they went along the road and across a field, until they came to a big log that was lying under a hickory tree, and there they both sat down side by side—plump!

Mr. A was still very cross, and Mr. P was still very hot and out of breath, so for a long while neither of them spoke. Then Mr. A looked round at Mr. P and gave a big sniff. And Mr. P looked at Mr. A, and he gave a sniff, too. And then they both began to wriggle their toes on the ground.

Presently Mr. P said:

"I shouldn't think you need be so mean, just because I did something to please you!"

And Mr. A said:

"Well, you didn't have to be so cross, just because I wanted to give you a s—surprise!"

"I only did it to make you laugh!" said Mr. P.

"I thought you'd be very pleased and m—merry!" said Mr. A.

Then Mr. A pulled a packet of lemon drops out of his apron pocket.

"Have one," he said to Mr. P.

Mr. P took it and sucked it, and then he pulled a little packet out of *his* apron pocket, and he said to Mr. A:

"Don't you want some chewing gum?"

Half an hour later, just as the sun was setting, anyone looking out of the front window might have seen two little figures, one very tall and thin and the other very short and stout, trudging arm in arm along the sidewalk.

They were Mr. A and Mr. P, going back to their grocery store.

And from what I can hear, they have never quarreled since.

26

"**W**HAT about going on a trip?" I said.

"Where?" Lee asked. She wouldn't just say yes to *any* trip.

"Oh, I don't know myself," I said, "I was thinking of Alaska, or Boston, or around the block."

"Oh Mother, not *really* around the block," Elinor said. "That's not a trip."

"It depends on who's going round it, I suppose," I said. "*You* always trip it. I can't keep up with you. No, I don't really mean around the block. I was thinking of just going somewhere to wear out the car so we would have to afford to buy a new one. We could keep going until it dropped to pieces. That might mean we'd get as far as Mexico City, but it might mean we'd only—"

The Drawbridge

BY LESLEY FROST

Illustrated by James Reid

"Get as far as Pittsfield?" Lee said.

"That's right," I said. "Or we might even stick on a hill half way. Shall we try?"

"Of course," they said together. So we tried.

But there were lots of difficulties to begin with. Elinor and Lee said they must take eighteen dolls apiece (not counting three hundred paper dolls), and all their crayons (even the broken ones), and the good victrola (with chiefly the Gilbert and Sullivan records). And I said I must take one hundred and fifty most important books and some cold cream. Then there was gum and candy (*not* licorice), and sun glasses, and playing cards, and the Tame Giraffe, and a frying pan and can opener in case we ran out of gas in the desert and no one

27

came along. Then Elinor and Lee *suddenly* said they had to take their three cousins—Prescott, Jackie, and Robin—and the three cousins said they had to take their three dogs. We were rather packed in, and quite heavy. We were so heavy we had four flat tires before I could manage to back out of the garage. They were very old tires. I suppose that was why. And they all blew out at once, which made such a noise the gas company called up to ask if it was the gas stove exploding, and the police department called up to ask who we thought we were shooting at. We said it was purely accidental, just our cannon had gone off before we were quite ready. Then we hung up, rather quickly I'm afraid, because we couldn't keep a straight face.

We ordered four new tires out of a big catalogue and sat in the garage for two weeks until they came. But it was fun sitting there because Lee and Robin began laughing when the police called up and simply couldn't stop. It was a two weeks' laugh. But the laugh was on us when the tires came and we remembered we had lost the jack and the wrench in Mexico last year. So we drove to a service station on the flat tires and let *it* do the changing. Elinor said we could have done that in the first place and saved two weeks. I suppose we could have, only we didn't think of it.

When we finally started, it was snowing in New England, hurricaning in Florida, sandstorming in Kansas, and earthquaking in California. The newspapers said so. We had to take care not to go there at least. We asked a policeman about it at the next corner, and we *thought* he said *Keep to the left*. The dogs were barking at the time, the cousins were singing, Elinor and Lee were arguing, and the Tame Giraffe had stopped being tame and was making faces at people out the back window (I could see him in the mirror). So no wonder I *thought* the policeman said "Keep to the left." Anyway we kept to the left and found ourselves in a pickle. There was mud up to the hubs, stones under the mud, rain coming down in buckets, lots of buzzards flying around, lots of Spanish moss hanging around, and a very wide river we couldn't get across.

"This must be Mississippi," Lee said.

"Mississippi or Mrs. Anybody," I said, "which ever it is, it's awful, even with new tires." And just then one of the fenders flew off and the fan belt snapped.

"We're going to pieces quite rapidly," Prescott remarked. "Do you think we'll make South America to-night?"

"Your sense of geography is extremely poor," I said, "and we'll be lucky if we cross this river at all. Oh, here's a bridge. That's *some*thing."

It certainly turned out to *be* something. It was a drawbridge, the longest drawbridge we had ever seen in all our travels, and it began to draw before we had quite reached the middle. We were hoisted up and up. We all held onto the car hard, hoping the car would take the hint and hold onto the bridge hard. But you can't teach an old car new tricks. We had been going nearly twenty miles an hour forward. Now we went at least fifty-five miles an hour backward. Just like a roller-coaster, only the wrong way round. Jackie said we would be dizzy—sick if we didn't turn our seats around, too, the way you can in trains. But the dogs were so tangled up with the seats, we couldn't manage. The dogs helped a little, though, by howling so much I didn't need to use the horn. Anyone could have heard us coming or going.

When we slowed down at last, I found I couldn't shut off the motor. The ignition was jammed (Prescott said something scientific about it that I couldn't understand), so before you could say Jack Robinson we were climbing that bridge again. It was miserable. I thought surely we would go over the edge. But the car didn't have the strength to make it. We climbed up hundreds of feet into the air on smooth asphalt, and then came *shooting* down backward again. We kept doing it—up and down, up and down, like a see-saw. We saw the bridge man running back and forth waving his arms at us to stop it. Prescott waved back. We were too far away, and going too fast to hear what he was saying. He looked like Charlie Chaplin being excited in a silent movie.

We *wanted* to stop in the worst way. This was wearing the car out much faster than was safe. We were squeaking all over. And pieces of us were coming off and rattling down like hail. Then a worse thing happened. We went up too fast and the front wheels caught over the top edge. We hung there.

"This is precarious," I said.

"What's precarious mean?" Lee asked from an upside-down-cake position.

"Risky," I said. "Don't ask questions when things are as precarious as this."

The bridge man thought it was precarious too. He com-

pletely lost his head when he saw us hanging on by the skin of our teeth like this and began lowering the drawbridge. That was a fatal mistake. It caught the boat just half through the opening and drove the masts down through the bottom, like one of those nursery pegs-and-hammer toys—you know the kind I mean. Elinor said it was the easiest and quickest way to make the boat look upside down. But the captain was quite angry. He and Jackie had a strong argument about it. But Lee said, "Oh, stop quarreling. Nobody is 'xactly to blame. This is just an accident."

I agreed with her that it was an accident in more ways than one, because when the bridge came down it caught our front wheels between the two sections and pinched them off as neat as a pin. Elinor said it was a clean cut anyway. But I saw that our trip was going to end right here in the middle of a drawbridge. So I asked the children to help make the best of a hard time. We decided to give the captain's children all of the candy and gum that was left over in order to make the captain feel better about the masts. And we gave Prescott's Mechano set to the bridge man because he was really mechanical-minded even if he *had* made two or three mistakes that afternoon. We gave the rest of the car to a farmer who lived along the river. He quickly attached some handles to the front and made a wheelbarrow. He had needed a wheelbarrow for some time.

Robin said, "Well, I guess the drawbridge isn't damaged very much."

"No," I said, "the drawbridge looks as good as ever. That's lucky for the drawbridge."

"But now *how* are we going to get home?" Lee asked.

"Why, in the new car, of course," I said. "What did you expect?"

31

"YES, Peter is clever." So said his mother; but then every goose thinks her own gosling a swan.

The minister and all of the people of the village said Peter was but a dull block. Maybe Peter *was* a fool; but, as the old saying goes, never a fool tumbles out of a tree but he lights on his toes. So now you shall hear how that Peter sold his two baskets of eggs for more than you or I could do, wise as we be.

"Peter," said his mother.

"Yes," said Peter, for he was well brought up, and always answered when he was spoken to.

"My dear little child, thou art wise, though so young now; how shall we get money to pay our rent?"

"Sell the eggs that the speckled hen has laid," said Peter.

"But when we have spent the money for them, what then?"

"Sell more eggs," said Peter, for he had an answer for everything.

Clever Peter and the Two Bottles

BY HOWARD PYLE

Illustrated by Howard Pyle

"But when the speckled hen lays no more eggs, what shall we do then?"

"We shall see," said Peter.

"Now indeed art thou wise," said his mother, "and I take thy meaning; it is this, when we have spent all, we must do as the little birds do, and trust in the good Heaven." Peter meant nothing of the kind, but then folks will think that such wise fellows as Peter and I mean more than we say, whence comes our wisdom.

32

So the next day Peter started off to the town, with the basket full of nice white eggs. The day was bright and warm and fair; the wind blew softly, and the wheat-fields lay like green velvet in the sun. The flowers were sprinkled all over the grass, and the bees kicked up their yellow legs as they tilted into them. The garlic stuck up stout spikes into the air, and the young radishes were green and lusty. The brown bird in the tree sang, "Cuckoo! cuckoo!" and Peter trudged contentedly along, kicking up little clouds of dust at every footstep, whistling merrily and staring up into the bright sky, where the white clouds hung like little sheep, feeding on the wide blue field. "If those clouds were sheep, and the sheep were mine, then I would be a great man and very proud," said Peter. But the clouds were clouds, and he was not a great man; nevertheless, he whistled more merrily than ever, for it was very nice to think of these things.

So he trudged along with great comfort until high noontide, against which time he had come nigh to the town, for he could see the red roofs and the tall spires peeping over the crest of the next green hill. By this time his stomach was crying, "Give! give!" for it longed for bread and cheese. Now, a great gray stone stood near by at the forking of the road, and just as Peter came to it he heard a noise. "Click! clack!" he turned his head, and, lo and behold! the side of the stone opened like a door, and out came a little old man dressed all in fine black velvet. "Good-day, Peter," said he. "Good-day, sir," said Peter, and he took off his hat as he spoke, for he could see with half an eye that this little old gentleman was none of your cheese-paring fine folks.

"Will you strike a bargain with me for your eggs?" said the little old man. Yes, Peter would strike a bargain; what would the little gentleman give him for his eggs? "I will give you

this," said the little old man, and he drew a black bottle out of his pocket.

Peter took the bottle and turned it over and over in his hands. "It is," said he, "a pretty little, good little, sweet little bottle, but it is not worth as much as my basket of eggs."

"Prut!" said the little gentleman, "now you are not talking like the wise Peter. You should never judge by the outside of things. What would you like to have?"

"I should like," said Peter, "to have a good dinner."

"Nothing easier!" said the little gentleman, and he drew the cork. Pop! pop! and what should come out of the bottle but two tall men, dressed all in blue with gold trimmings. "What will you have, sir?" said the first of these to the little gentleman.

"A good dinner for two," said the little man.

No sooner said than done; for, before you could say Frederic Strutzenwillenbachen, there stood a table, with a sweet, clean, white cloth spread over it, and on this was the nicest dinner that you ever saw, for there were beer and chitterlings, and cheese and good white bread, fit for the king. Then Peter and the little man fell to with might and main, and ate till they could eat no more. After they were done, the two tall men took table and dishes and all back into the bottle again, and the little gentleman corked it up.

34

"Yes," said Peter, "I will give you my basket of eggs for the little black bottle." And so the bargain was struck. Then Peter started off home, and the little man went back again into the great stone and closed the door behind him. He took the basket of eggs with him; where he took it neither Peter nor I will ever be able to tell you.

So Peter trudged along homeward, until, after a while, the day waxing warm, he grew tired. "I wish," said he, "that I had a fine white horse to ride."

Then he took the cork out of the bottle. Pop! pop! and out came the two tall fellows, just as they had done for the little old man. "What will you have, sir?" said the first of them.

"I will have," said Peter, "a fine white horse to ride."

No sooner said than done; for there, before him in the road, stood a fine white horse, with a long mane and tail, just like so much spun silk. In his mouth was a silver bit; on his back was a splendid saddle, covered all over with gold and jewels; on his feet were shoes of pure gold, so that he was a very handsome horse indeed.

Peter mounted on his great horse and rode away home, as grand as though he were a lord or a nobleman.

Every one whom he met stopped in the middle of the road and looked after him. "Just look at Peter!" cried they; but Peter held his chin very high, and rode along without looking at them, for he knew what a fine sight he was on his white horse.

And so he came home again.

"What didst thou get for thy eggs, my little duck?" said his mother.

"I got a bottle, mother," said Peter.

Then at first Peter's mother began to think as others thought, that Peter was a dull block. But when she saw what a wonderful bottle it was, and how it held many good things and one over, she changed her mind again, and thought that her Peter was as wise as the moon.

And now nothing was lacking in the cottage; if Peter and his mother wanted this, it came to them; if they wished for that, the two tall men in the bottle fetched it. They lined the house all inside with pure gold, and built the chimneys of bricks of silver, so that there was nothing so fine between all the four great rivers. Peter dressed in satin and his mother in silk, and everybody called him "Lord Peter." Even the minister of the village said that he was no dull boy, for nobody is dull who rides on horseback and never wears wooden shoes. So now Peter was a rich man.

One morning Peter said to his mother, "Mother, I am going to ask the King to let me marry his daughter."

To this his mother said nothing, for surely her Peter was as good as any princess that ever lived.

So off Peter rode, dressed all in his best and seated astride of a grand horse. At last he came to the palace, which was finer than the handsome new house of Herr Mayor Kopff. Rap! rap! rap! Peter knocked at the door, and presently came a neat servant girl and opened it to him. "Is the King at home, my dear?" said Peter.

Yes, the King was at home; would he come into the parlor and sit down? So Peter went into the parlor and sat down, and then the King came in, dressed in his best dressing-gown, with silver slippers upon his feet, and a golden crown upon his head.

"What is your name?" said the King.

"Peter Stulzenmilchen," said Peter.

"And what do you want, Lord Peter," said the King; for, as I have said, Peter was dressed in his best clothes, and the old King thought that he was a great lord.

"I want to marry your daughter," said Peter.

36

To this the King said "Hum-m-m," and Peter said nothing. Then the King said that he had determined that no one should marry his daughter without bringing him a basketful of diamonds, rubies, topazes, emeralds, pearls, and all manner of precious stones; for he thought by this to get rid of Peter.

"Is that all?" said Peter. "Nothing is easier."

So off he went, until he came to a chestnut woods just back of the royal kitchen-garden. There he uncorked his bottle. Pop! pop! and out came the two tall men. "What will you have, sir?" said they. Peter told them what he wanted, and it was no sooner said than done; for, there on the ground before him, stood a basket full of all kinds of precious stones; each of them was as large as a hen's egg, and over all of them was spread a nice clean white napkin. So Peter took the basket on his arm and went back again to the palace.

But how the King did open his eyes, to be sure, and how he stared! "Now," said Peter, "I should like to marry your daughter, if you please."

At this the King hemmed and hawed again. No, Peter could not marry the Princess yet, for the King had determined that no man should marry his daughter without bringing him a bird all of pure silver that could sing whenever it was wanted, and that more sweetly than a nightingale; for he thought that now he should be rid of Peter, at any rate.

"Nothing easier," said Peter, and off he went again.

When he had come to the chestnut woods, he uncorked his bottle and told the two tall men what he wanted. No sooner said than done; for there was a bird all of pure silver. And not only that, but the bird sat in a little golden tree, and the leaves of the tree were emeralds, and rubies hung like cherries from the branches.

Then Peter wrapped this up in his handkerchief and took

it to the palace. As for the King, he could not look at it or listen to it enough.

"Now," said Peter, "I should like to marry your daughter, if you please."

But at this the King sang the same tune again. No, Peter could not marry his daughter yet, for the King had determined that the man who was to marry his daughter should first bring him a golden sword, so keen that it could cut a feather floating in the air, yet so strong that it could cut through an iron bar.

"Nothing easier," said Peter, and this time the men of the bottle brought him such a sword as he asked for, and the hilt was studded all over with precious stones, so that it was very handsome indeed. Then Peter brought it to the King, and it did as the King would have it—it cut through a feather floating in the air; as for the iron bar, it cut through that as easily as you would bite through a radish.

And now it seemed as though there was nothing else to be done but to let Peter marry the Princess. So the King asked him in to supper, and they all three sat down together, the King and the Princess and Peter. And it was a fine feast, I can tell you, for they had both white and red wine, besides sausages and cheese, and real white bread and puddings, and all manner of good things; for kings and princesses eat and drink of the best.

As for Peter, he made eyes at the Princess, and the Princess looked down on her plate and blushed, and Peter thought that he had never seen such a pretty girl.

After a while the King began to question Peter how he came by all these fine things—the precious stones, the silver bird, and the golden sword; but no, Peter would not tell. Then the King and the Princess begged and begged him, until, at

last, Peter lost his wits and told all about the bottle. Then the King said nothing more, and presently, it being nine o'clock, Peter went to bed. After he had gone the King and the Princess put their heads together, and the end of the matter was that the wicked King went to Peter's room and stole the bottle from under the pillow where he had hidden it, and put one in its place that was as empty as a beer barrel after the soldiers have been in the town; for the King and the Princess thought that it would be a fine thing to have the bottle for themselves.

When the next morning had come, and they were all sitting at their breakfast together, the King said, "Now, Lord Peter, let us see what your bottle will do; give us such and such a kind of wine."

"Nothing easier," said Peter. Then he uncorked the bottle, but not so much as a single dead fly came out of it.

"But where is the wine?" said the King.

"I do not know," said Peter.

At this the King called him hard names and turned him out of the palace, neck and heels; so back poor Peter went to his mother with a flea in his ear, as the saying is. Now he was poor again, and everybody called him a dull block, for he rode no great white horse and he wore wooden shoes.

"Never mind," said his mother, "here is another basket of eggs from the speckled hen." So Peter set off with these to the market town, as he had done with the others before. When he had come to the great stone at the forking of the road, whom should he meet but the same little gentleman he had met the first time. "Will you strike a bargain?" said he. Yes, Peter would strike a bargain, and gladly. Thereupon the little old man brought out another black bottle.

"Two men are in this bottle," said the little old man; "when they have done all that you want them to do, say 'brikket-ligg' and they will go back again. Will you trade with me?" Yes, Peter would trade. So Peter gave the little man the eggs, and the little man gave Peter the second bottle, and they parted very good friends.

After a while Peter grew tired. "Now," said he to himself, "I will ride a little;" and so he drew the cork out of the bottle. Pop! pop! out came two men from the bottle; but this time they were ugly and black, and each held a stout stick in his hand. They said not a word, but, without more ado, fell upon Peter and began threshing him as though he was wheat on the barn floor. "Stop! stop!" cried Peter, and he went hopping and skipping up and down, and here and there, but it seemed as though the two ugly black men did not hear him, for the blows fell as thick as hail on the roof. At last he gathered his wits together, like a flock of pigeons, and cried, "Brikket-ligg! brikket-ligg!" Then, whisk! pop! they went back into the bottle again, and Peter corked it up, and corked it tightly, I can tell you.

The next day he started off to the palace once more. Rap! rap! rap! he knocked at the door. Was the King at home? Yes, the King was at home; would he come and sit in the parlor?

Presently the King came in, in dressing-gown and slippers. "What! are you back again?" said he.

"Yes; I am back again," said Peter.

"What do you want?" said the King.

"I want to marry the Princess," said Peter.

"What have you brought this time?" said the King.

"I have brought another bottle," said Peter.

Then the King rubbed his hands and was very polite indeed, and asked Peter in to breakfast, and Peter went. So they all three sat down together, the King, the Princess, and Peter.

"My dear," said the King, to the Princess, "the Lord Peter has brought another bottle with him." Thereat the Princess was very polite also. Would Lord Peter let them see the bottle? Oh yes! Peter would do that; so he drew it out of his pocket and sat it upon the table.

Perhaps they would like to have it opened. Yes, that they would. So Peter opened the bottle.

Hui! what a hubbub there was! The King hopped about till his slippers flew off, his dressing-gown fluttered like great wings, and his crown rolled off from his head and across the floor, like a quoit at the fair. As for the Princess, she never danced in all of her life as she danced that morning. They made such a noise that the soldiers of the Royal Guard came running in; but the two tall black men spared them no more than the King and the Princess. Then came all of the Lords of the Council, and they likewise danced to the same music as the rest.

"Oh, Peter! dear Lord Peter! cork up your men again!" they all cried.

"Will you give me back my bottle?" said Peter.

"Yes! yes!" cried the King.

"Will you marry me?" said Peter.

"Yes! yes!" cried the Princess.

Then Peter said "brikket-ligg!" and the two tall men popped back into the bottle again. So the King gave him back his other bottle, and the minister was called in and married him to the Princess.

After that he lived happily, and when the old King died he became King over all of the land. As for the Princess, she was as good a wife as you ever saw, but Peter always kept the bottle near to him—maybe that was the reason.

Ah me! if I could only take my eggs to such a
market and get two such bottles for them!
What would I do with them? It would
take too long to tell you.

THERE was a table set out under a tree in front of the house, and the March Hare and the Hatter were having tea at it: a Dormouse was sitting between them, fast asleep, and the other two were using it as a cushion, resting their elbows on it, and talking over its head. "Very uncomfortable for the Dormouse," thought Alice; "only, as it's asleep, I suppose it doesn't mind."

The table was a large one, but the three were all crowded together at one corner of it. "No room! No room!" they cried out when they saw Alice coming. "There's *plenty* of room!" said Alice indignantly, and she sat down in a large arm-chair at one end of the table.

"Have some wine," the March Hare said in an encouraging tone.

Alice looked all round the table, but there was nothing on it but tea. "I don't see any wine," she remarked.

"There isn't any," said the March Hare.

A Mad Tea-Party

BY LEWIS CARROLL

Illustrated by John Tenniel

"Then it wasn't very civil of you to offer it," said Alice angrily.

"It wasn't very civil of you to sit down without being invited," said the March Hare.

"I didn't know it was *your* table," said Alice; "it's laid for a great many more than three."

"Your hair wants cutting," said the Hatter. He had been looking at Alice for some time with great curiosity, and this was his first speech.

43

"You should learn not to make personal remarks," Alice said with some severity; "it's very rude."

The Hatter opened his eyes very wide on hearing this; but all he *said* was, "Why is a raven like a writing-desk?"

"Come, we shall have some fun now!" thought Alice. "I'm glad they've begun asking riddles—I believe I can guess that," she added aloud.

"Do you mean that you think you can find out the answer to it?" said the March Hare.

"Exactly so," said Alice.

"Then you should say what you mean," the March Hare went on.

"I do," Alice hastily replied; "at least—at least I mean what I say—that's the same thing, you know."

"Not the same thing a bit!" said the Hatter. "Why, you might just as well say that 'I see what I eat' is the same thing as 'I eat what I see'!"

"You might just as well say," added the March Hare, "that 'I like what I get' is the same thing as 'I get what I like'!"

"You might just as well say," added the Dormouse, who seemed to be talking in his sleep, "that 'I breathe when I sleep' is the same thing as 'I sleep when I breathe'!"

"It *is* the same thing with you," said the Hatter, and here the conversation dropped, and the party sat silent for a minute, while Alice thought over all she could remember about ravens and writing-desks, which wasn't much.

The Hatter was the first to break the silence. "What day of the month is it?" he said, turning to Alice; he had taken his watch out of his pocket, and was looking at it uneasily, shaking it every now and then, and holding it to his ear.

Alice considered a little, and then said, "The fourth."

"Two days wrong!" sighed the Hatter. "I told you butter wouldn't suit the works!" he added, looking angrily at the March Hare.

"It was the *best* butter," the March Hare meekly replied.

"Yes, but some crumbs must have got in as well," the Hatter grumbled; "you shouldn't have put it in with the bread-knife."

The March Hare took the watch and looked at it gloomily: then he dipped it into his cup of tea, and looked at it again: but he could think of nothing better to say than his first remark, "It was the *best* butter, you know."

Alice had been looking over his shoulder with some curiosity. "What a funny watch!" she remarked. "It tells the day of the month, and doesn't tell what o'clock it is!"

"Why should it?" muttered the Hatter. "Does *your* watch tell you what year it is?"

"Of course not," Alice replied very readily: "but that's because it stays the same year for such a long time together."

"Which is just the case with *mine,*" said the Hatter.

Alice felt dreadfully puzzled. The Hatter's remark seemed to her to have no sort of meaning in it, and yet it was certainly English. "I don't quite understand you," she said, as politely as she could.

"The Dormouse is asleep again," said the Hatter, and he poured a little hot tea on to its nose.

The Dormouse shook its head impatiently, and said, without opening its eyes, "Of course, of course, just what I was going to remark myself."

"Have you guessed the riddle yet?" the Hatter said, turning to Alice again.

"No, I give it up," Alice replied. "What's the answer?"

"I haven't the slightest idea," said the Hatter.

"Nor I," said the March Hare.

Alice sighed wearily. "I think you might do something better with the time," she said, "than wasting it in asking riddles that have no answers."

"If you knew Time as well as I do," said the Hatter, "you wouldn't talk about wasting *it*. It's *him*."

"I don't know what you mean," said Alice.

"Of course you don't!" the Hatter said, tossing his head contemptuously. "I dare say you never even spoke to Time!"

"Perhaps not," Alice cautiously replied; "but I know I have to beat time when I learn music."

"Ah! that accounts for it," said the Hatter. "He won't stand beating. Now, if you only kept on good terms with him, he'd do almost anything you liked with the clock. For instance, suppose it were nine o'clock in the morning, just time to begin lessons; you'd only have to whisper a hint to Time, and round goes the clock in a twinkling! Half-past one, time for dinner!"

46

("I only wish it was," the March Hare said to itself in a whisper.)

"That would be grand, certainly," said Alice thoughtfully; "but then—I shouldn't be hungry for it, you know."

"Not at first, perhaps," said the Hatter, "but you could keep it to half-past one as long as you liked."

"Is that the way *you* manage?" Alice asked.

The Hatter shook his head mournfully. "Not I!" he replied. "We quarrelled last March—just before *he* went mad, you know—" (pointing with his teaspoon at the March Hare), "—it was at the great concert given by the Queen of Hearts, and I had to sing

> *'Twinkle, twinkle, little bat!*
> *How I wonder what what you're at!'*

You know the song perhaps?"

"I've heard something like it," said Alice.

"It goes on, you know," the Hatter continued, "in this way:—

> *'Up above the world you fly,*
> *Like a teatray in the sky.*
> *Twinkle, twinkle—'"*

Here the Dormouse shook itself, and began singing in its sleep *"Twinkle, twinkle, twinkle, twinkle—"* and went on so long that they had to pinch it to make it stop.

"Well, I'd hardly finished the first verse," said the Hatter, "when the Queen bawled out, 'He's murdering the time! Off with his head!'"

"How dreadfully savage!" exclaimed Alice.

"And ever since that," the Hatter went on in a mournful tone, "he won't do a thing I ask! It's always six o'clock now."

A bright idea came into Alice's head. "Is that the reason so many tea-things are put out here?" she asked.

"Yes, that's it," said the Hatter with a sigh; "it's always tea-time, and we've no time to wash the things between whiles."

"Then you keep moving round, I suppose?" said Alice.

"Exactly so," said the Hatter, "as the things get used up."

"But when you come to the beginning again?" Alice ventured to ask.

"Suppose we change the subject," the March Hare interrupted, yawning. "I'm getting tired of this. I vote the young lady tells us a story."

"I'm afraid I don't know one," said Alice, rather alarmed at the proposal.

"Then the Dormouse shall!" they both cried. "Wake up, Dormouse!" And they pinched it on both sides at once.

The Dormouse slowly opened his eyes. "I wasn't asleep," he said in a hoarse, feeble voice, "I heard every word you fellows were saying."

"Tell us a story!" said the March Hare.

"Yes, please do!" pleaded Alice.

"And be quick about it," added the Hatter, "or you'll be asleep again before it's done."

"Once upon a time there were three little sisters," the Dormouse began in a great hurry; "and their names were Elsie, Lacie, and Tillie; and they lived at the bottom of a well—"

"What did they live on?" said Alice, who always took a great interest in questions of eating and drinking.

48

"They lived on treacle," said the Dormouse, after thinking a minute or two.

"They couldn't have done that, you know," Alice gently remarked. "They'd have been ill."

"So they were," said the Dormouse; "*very* ill."

Alice tried a little to fancy to herself what such an extraordinary way of living would be like, but it puzzled her too much, so she went on: "But why did they live at the bottom of a well?"

"Take some more tea," the March Hare said to Alice, very earnestly.

"I've had nothing yet," Alice replied in an offended tone, "so I can't take more."

"You mean, you can't take *less*," said the Hatter: "it's very easy to take *more* than nothing."

"Nobody asked *your* opinion," said Alice.

"Who's making personal remarks now?" the Hatter asked triumphantly.

Alice did not quite know what to say to this, so she helped herself to some tea and bread-and-butter, and then turned to the Dormouse, and repeated her question. "Why did they live at the bottom of a well?"

The Dormouse again took a minute or two to think about it, and then said, "It was a treacle-well."

"There's no such thing!" Alice was beginning very angrily, but the Hatter and the March Hare went "Sh! sh!" and the Dormouse sulkily remarked, "If you can't be civil, you'd better finish the story for yourself."

"No, please go on!" Alice said very humbly. "I won't interrupt you again. I dare say there may be *one!*"

"One, indeed!" said the Dormouse indignantly. However,

he consented to go on. "And so these three little sisters—they were learning to draw, you know—"

"What did they draw?" said Alice, quite forgetting her promise.

"Treacle," said the Dormouse, without considering at all this time.

"I want a clean cup," interrupted the Hatter; "let's all move one place on."

He moved on as he spoke, and the Dormouse followed him, the March Hare moved into the Dormouse's place, and Alice rather unwillingly took the place of the March Hare. The Hatter was the only one who got any advantage from the change, and Alice was a good deal worse off than before, as the March Hare had just upset the milk-jug into his plate.

Alice did not wish to offend the Dormouse again, so she began very cautiously: "But I don't understand. Where did they draw the treacle from?"

"You can draw water out of a water-well," said the Hatter; "so I should think you could draw treacle out of a treacle-well—eh, stupid?"

"But they were *in* the well," Alice said to the Dormouse, not choosing to notice this last remark.

"Of course they were," said the Dormouse, ——"well in."

This answer so confused poor Alice, that she let the Dormouse go on for some time without interrupting it.

"They were learning to draw," the Dormouse went on, yawning and rubbing its eyes, for it was getting very sleepy; "and they drew all manner of things—everything that begins with an M—"

"Why with an M?" said Alice.

"Why not?" said the March Hare.

Alice was silent.

50

The Dormouse had closed its eyes by this time, and was going off into a doze; but, on being pinched by the Hatter, it woke up again with a little shriek, and went on: "—that begins with an M, such as mousetraps, and the moon, and memory, and muchness—you know you say things are 'much of a muchness'—did you ever see such a thing as a drawing of a muchness?"

"Really, now you ask me," said Alice, very much confused, "I don't think—"

"Then you shouldn't talk," said the Hatter.

This piece of rudeness was more than Alice could bear; she got up in great disgust, and walked off. The Dormouse fell asleep instantly, and neither of the others took the least notice of her going, though she looked back once or twice, half hoping that they would call after her. The last time she saw them, they were trying to put the Dormouse into the teapot.

"At any rate I'll never go *there* again!" said Alice as she picked her way through the wood.

"It's the stupidest tea-party I ever was at in all my life!"

51

"**O**H, ALLAH! I need money! I need one thousand ghurush!" The wheedling voice of Nasr-ed-Din Hodja rose from behind his courtyard walls, built high of sun-dried brick of clay and straw. Whether or not the prayer rose to the ears of Allah, it was loud enough for the ears of the neighbors.

Siraj-ed-Din Bey, the wealthy merchant whose yard adjoined the Hodja's, looked from his upstairs window. He could see Nasr-ed-Din Hodja kneeling on a well-worn prayer rug, sitting erect, then bowing repeatedly till his forehead touched the ground, as he murmured his prayer again and again.

"Oh, Allah! I need money— much money. I need one thousand ghurush. Eight hundred ghurush would not be enough. nor nine hundred, nor nine hundred and ninety-nine. I must have exactly one thousand ghurush. A smaller sum I could not possibly accept. Oh, Allah, send me one thousand ghurush—and may it come soon."

Money from the Sky

BY ALICE GEER KELSEY

Illustrated by Frank Dobias

Siraj-ed-Din Bey, listening in his open window, smiled as he would have smiled at a child praying for a large piece of rahat lokum. He smiled at the Hodja's queer idea of prayer. Siraj-ed-Din Bey knew that if a man really wanted something, he had to mix work with his prayers.

The voice chanted on, "One thousand ghurush, Allah! Not one coin less than a thousand!"

"It is time to teach that simple old Hodja not to pray without helping Allah to make his prayers come true," thought

52

Siraj-ed-Din Bey, who was really fond of his kindly neighbor. He laughed as a scheme grew in his mind.

Turning noiselessly from his high window, Siraj-ed-Din Bey hurried to the room where his money was hidden. Carefully he counted out nine hundred and ninety-nine ghurush. He recounted it to be sure there was not a single coin more or less. He put the money in a bag, tied it securely, and tiptoed back to the open window. His stockinged feet on his thick rugs made not a sound. Taking careful aim, he tossed the money bag. It barely missed the Hodja's bowed head and landed with a merry chinking on the cobblestones. Then Siraj-ed-Din Bey hurried to his wife's room, where he could watch unseen from behind her latticed window.

Without waiting to thank Allah, Nasr-ed-Din Hodja began counting the money. He counted it again and again. He tried to divide it into ten piles of one hundred ghurush each, but, no matter how many times he counted, one pile had but ninety-nine coins.

Siraj-ed-Din Bey and his wife, peering unseen through the latticed window, clapped their hands tightly over their mouths to hold back the laughter.

"I will let him count once more," whispered Siraj-ed-Din Bey to his wife. "Then I will explain the joke to him. He will laugh as hard as we."

But Siraj-ed-Din Bey had waited too long. Nasr-ed-Din Hodja did not count the coins again. Instead, he put them all

snugly to rest in the money bag, tied the bag securely, and tucked it out of sight in his wide girdle. Then he knelt on the prayer rug.

"Oh, Allah!" prayed the Hodja. "You did not count the ghurush correctly. There were not quite one thousand. You owe me one more ghurush. Send me that whenever it is convenient. And thanks, many thanks, for the nine hundred and ninety-nine you did send me."

If it had not been for the lattice, Siraj-ed-Din Bey would have leaped through his window without bothering about stairs or gates. Passers-by gaped to see the wealthiest merchant of Ak Shehir rush from his door as though pursued by jackals and bang on Hodja's street gate. When the street door was pulled open for him, Siraj-ed-Din Bey shot through it toward the Hodja.

"Give me back my money bag!" shouted Siraj-ed-Din Bey, too excited to care who heard. He did not notice the open-mouthed crowd gathering at the Hodja's gate. "Give me back my nine hundred and ninety-nine ghurush!"

"Your money bag? Your nine hundred and ninety-nine ghurush?"

"Yes, mine! I tossed them over the wall just for a joke. You said you would not accept less than a thousand ghurush. I was just trying to show you how silly such a prayer must sound to Allah."

"You tossed it? No, indeed! The money bag was a gift from Allah. It fell directly from heaven in answer to my prayer."

"I will take you and the money bag to court," said Siraj-ed-Din Bey, laying an angry hand on Nasr-ed-Din Hodja's shoulder. "We'll soon see whether it fell from heaven or from my window!"

54

"Yes, we'll have it decided in court." The Hodja always relished the court, with its chances for talk and excitement. "You will soon learn that this money fell from heaven."

"Well, hurry! Haidi bakalim!" Siraj-ed-Din Bey took a step toward the gate, but the Hodja hesitated.

"My coat! Fatima is mending it. I cannot go to court without it." The Hodja looked down at his shabby clothes.

"I will lend you a coat."

"But my donkey! She has a lame foot. I cannot ride her a long distance and, of course, we are in too much of a hurry to walk."

"I will lend you a horse."

"But a saddle and bridle! My little donkey's would never fit your big horse."

"I will lend you a saddle and bridle. Come into my yard and I will fit you out for the trip to court."

Nasr-ed-Din Hodja rolled up his prayer rug and put it away. He waved good-bye toward his wife's latticed window. He could not see her, but he knew her well enough to be sure she was not missing a word or a gesture. Then he followed Siraj-ed-Din Bey.

In a short time the two men left the merchant's house on horseback. The merchant had supplied Nasr-ed-Din Hodja with a spirited dappled gray, which he rode as though it were a donkey. The Hodja bowed to left and to right as he went bouncing through the streets in his borrowed grandeur. He felt very high and mighty, but the men in the streets knew it would take more than an expensive coat, an embroidered saddle, a jingling bridle, and a fine horse to make a dashing horseman of the Hodja.

Arriving at the court, Siraj-ed-Din Bey lost no time in telling his story to the Judge. As he talked, he was disturbed at

55

the strange way the Hodja was watching him, smiling sadly and shaking his head slowly.

"Well, Nasr-ed-Din Hodja," said the Judge, "have you anything to say?"

"Poor Siraj-ed-Din Bey," sighed the Hodja, his voice fairly dripping sympathy. "How sad! How very, very sad! He was such a good neighbor and so highly respected by all! To think that he should have lost his mind!"

"Lost his mind?" snapped the Judge. "What do you mean?"

"Oh, didn't you know?" The Hodja went close to the Judge and whispered in a voice that could be heard throughout the room, "He thinks everything belongs to him. You heard his story about my money bag. Just try him on something else, and he will be sure to say it is his. Ask him whose coat this is I have on my back."

"My coat, of course," exclaimed the merchant, not waiting for the Judge to ask. "The Hodja knows it is my coat."

The Hodja shook his head sadly. "Try something else, Judge. Ask him, for instance, whose saddle is on my dappled gray horse."

"My saddle, of course, and it's my bridle too," cried Siraj-ed-Din Bey. "The Hodja knows they are both mine."

"You see how pathetic it is," said the Hodja with a deep sigh of pity. "Poor man! He is so crazy that he might even claim my fine dappled gray horse."

"Of course I claim the horse," shouted the merchant. "I have owned that dappled gray since it was a colt."

The Hodja shrugged his shoulders. The Judge had evidence enough; let him decide.

"This is a strange case—a sad case," said the Judge thoughtfully. It was not easy to condemn the richest man in all

Ak Shehir. "I believed Siraj-ed-Din Bey about tossing the money bag, though it was a rather wild story. Now I see differently. When he claims to own the Hodja's very coat and horse, saddle and bridle, he shows his mind is unbalanced. Siraj-ed-Din Bey, I suggest that you go home and take a good long rest. You have been working too hard, I am sure. Nasr-ed-Din Hodja, you may keep your money bag and all of your possessions that your unfortunate neighbor is trying to claim."

The two men rode in silence through the streets of Ak Shehir. Siraj-ed-Din Bey's shoulders sagged as though he had suddenly become an old man. Nasr-ed-Din Hodja bounced and gyrated with every step of the proud horse who was so unlike his donkey.

The merchant rode in at his own gate and turned to close it after himself. To his surprise, he was not alone. He was followed by the warmly grinning Hodja.

"Here is your money bag," said the Hodja, handing the heavy bag to the surprised merchant. "And your coat. And your horse with his saddle and bridle."

Siraj-ed-Din Bey, holding the money bag in one hand and the bridle of the dappled gray in the other, stared at the beaming Hodja, but could think of not a word to say.

"Wasn't it fun to fool that pompous old Judge?" chuckled the Hodja. "I am going right back to court to tell him it was all a joke—that things are not always what the evidence makes them seem."

Siraj-ed-Din Bey revived quickly, to say, "Ride my horse back."

"Oh, no. My donkey's lameness is surely gone by now, and Fatima has probably mended my coat."

58

JONAS JONAS HUCKABUCK was a farmer in Nebraska with a wife, Mama Mama Huckabuck and a daughter, Pony Pony Huckabuck.

"Your father gave you two names the same in front," people had said to him.

And he answered, "Yes, two names are easier to remember. If you call me by my first name Jonas and I don't hear you then when you call me by my second name Jonas maybe I will.

"And," he went on, "I call my pony-face girl Pony Pony because if she doesn't hear me the first time she always does the second."

And so they lived on a farm where they raised pop corn, these three, Jonas Jonas Huckabuck, his wife, Mama Mama Huckabuck and their pony-face daughter, Pony Pony Huckabuck.

After they harvested the crop one year they had the barns, the cribs, the sheds, the shacks and all the cracks and corners of the farm, all filled with pop corn.

"We came out to Nebraska to raise pop corn," said Jonas Jonas, "and I guess we got nearly enough pop corn this year for the pop corn poppers and all the friends and relations of all the pop corn poppers in these United States."

And this was the year Pony Pony was going to bake her first squash pie all by herself. In one corner of the corn crib, all covered over with pop corn, she had a secret, a big round

The Huckabuck Family
and how they raised Pop Corn

BY CARL SANDBURG

Illustrated by Maud and Miska Petersham

squash, a fat yellow squash, a rich squash all spotted with spots of gold.

She carried the squash into the kitchen, took a long sharp shining knife, and then she cut the squash in the middle till she had two big half squashes. And inside just like outside it was rich yellow spotted with spots of gold.

And there was a shine of silver. And Pony Pony wondered why silver should be in a squash. She picked and plunged with her fingers till she pulled it out.

"It's a buckle," she said, "a silver buckle, a Chinese silver slipper buckle."

She ran with it to her father and said, "Look what I found when I cut open the golden yellow squash spotted with gold spots—it is a Chinese silver slipper buckle."

"It means our luck is going to change, and we don't know whether it will be good luck or bad luck," said Jonas Jonas to his daughter, Pony Pony Huckabuck.

Then she ran with it to her mother and said, "Look what I found when I cut open the yellow squash spotted with spots of gold—it is a Chinese silver slipper buckle."

"It means our luck is going to change, and we don't know whether it will be good luck or bad luck," said Mama Mama Huckabuck.

And that night a fire started in the barns, cribs, sheds, shacks, cracks and corners, where the pop corn harvest was kept. All night long the pop corn popped. In the morning the ground all around the farm house and the barn was covered with white pop corn so it looked like a heavy fall of snow.

All the next day the fire kept on and the pop corn popped till it was up to the shoulders of Pony Pony when she tried to walk from the house to the barn. And that night in all the barns, cribs, sheds, shacks, cracks and corners of the farm, the pop corn went on popping.

In the morning when Jonas Jonas Huckabuck looked out of the upstairs window he saw the pop corn popping and coming higher and higher. It was nearly up to the window. Before evening and dark of that day, Jonas Jonas Huckabuck, and his wife Mama Mama Huckabuck and their daughter Pony Pony Huckabuck, all went away from the farm saying, "We came to Nebraska to raise pop corn, but this is too much. We will not come back till the wind blows away the pop corn. We will not come back till we get a sign and a signal."

They went to Oskaloosa, Iowa. And the next year Pony Pony Huckabuck was very proud because when she stood on the sidewalks in the street she could see her father sitting high on the seat of a coal wagon, driving two big spanking horses hitched with shining brass harness in front of the coal wagon. And though Pony Pony and Jonas Jonas were proud, very proud all that year, there never came a sign, a signal.

The next year again was a proud year, exactly as proud a year as they spent in Oskaloosa. They went to Paducah, Kentucky, to Defiance, Ohio; Peoria, Illinois; Indianapolis, Indiana; Walla Walla, Washington. And in all these places Pony Pony Huckabuck saw her father, Jonas Jonas Huckabuck, standing in rubber boots deep down in a ditch with a shining steel shovel shoveling yellow clay and black mud from down in the ditch high and high up over his shoulders. And though it was a proud year they got no sign, no signal.

The next year came. It was the proudest of all. This was the year Jonas Jonas Huckabuck and his family lived in Elgin, Illinois, and Jonas Jonas was watchman in a watch factory watching the watches.

"I know where you have been," Mama Mama Huckabuck would say of an evening to Pony Pony Huckabuck. "You have been down to the watch factory watching your father watch the watches."

"Yes," said Pony Pony. "Yes, and this evening when I was watching father watch the watches in the watch factory, I looked over my left shoulder and I saw a policeman with a star and brass buttons and he was watching me to see if I was watching father watch the watches in the watch factory."

It was a proud year. Pony Pony saved her money. Thanksgiving came. Pony Pony said, "I am going to get a squash to

make a squash pie." She hunted from one grocery to another; she kept her eyes on the farm wagons coming into Elgin with squashes.

She found what she wanted, the yellow squash spotted

with gold spots. She took it home, cut it open, and saw the inside was like the outside, all rich yellow spotted with gold spots.

There was a shine like silver. She picked and plunged with her fingers and pulled and pulled till at last she pulled out the shine of silver.

"It's a sign; it is a signal," she said. "It is a buckle, a slipper buckle, a Chinese silver slipper buckle. It is the mate to the other buckle. Our luck is going to change. Yoo hoo! Yoo hoo!"

She told her father and mother about the buckle. They went back to the farm in Nebraska. The wind by this time had been blowing and blowing for three years, and all the pop corn was blown away.

"Now we are going to be farmers again," said Jonas Jonas Huckabuck to Mama Mama Huckabuck and to Pony Pony Huckabuck. "And we are going to raise cabbages, beets and turnips; we are going to raise squash, rutabaga, pumpkins and peppers for pickling. We are going to raise wheat, oats, barley, rye. We are going to raise corn such as Indian corn and kaffir corn—but we are not going to raise any pop corn for the pop corn poppers to be popping."

And the pony-face daughter, Pony Pony Huckabuck, was proud because she had on new black slippers, and around her ankles, holding the slippers on the left foot and the right foot, she had two buckles, silver buckles, Chinese silver slipper buckles. They were mates.

Sometimes on Thanksgiving Day and Christmas and New Year's, she tells her friends to be careful when they open a squash.

"Squashes make your luck change good to bad and bad to good," says Pony Pony.

63

ONE day, when Christopher Robin and Winnie-the-Pooh and Piglet were all talking together, Christopher Robin finished the mouthful he was eating and said carelessly: "I saw a Heffalump to-day, Piglet."

"What was it doing?" asked Piglet.

"Just lumping along," said Christopher Robin. "I don't think it saw *me*."

"I saw one once," said Piglet. "At least, I think I did," he said. "Only perhaps it wasn't."

"So did I," said Pooh, wondering what a Heffalump was like.

"You don't often see them," said Christopher Robin carelessly.

"Not now," said Piglet.

"Not at this time of year," said Pooh.

Then they all talked about something else, until it was time for Pooh and Piglet to go home together. At first as they stumped along the path which edged the Hundred Acre Wood, they didn't say much to each other; but when they came to the stream and had helped each other across the stepping stones, and were able to walk side by side again over the heather, they began to talk in a friendly way about this and that, and Piglet said, "If you see what I mean, Pooh," and Pooh said, "It's just what I think myself, Piglet," and Piglet said, "But, on the other hand, Pooh, we must remember," and Pooh said, "Quite true, Piglet, although I had forgotten it for the moment." And

Piglet Meets a Heffalump

BY A. A. MILNE

Illustrated by
Ernest H. Shepard

then, just as they came to the Six Pine Trees, Pooh looked round to see that nobody else was listening, and said in a very solemn voice:

"Piglet, I have decided something."

"What have you decided, Pooh?"

"I have decided to catch a Heffalump."

Pooh nodded his head several times as he said this, and waited for Piglet to say "How?" or "Pooh, you couldn't!" or something helpful of that sort, but Piglet said nothing. The fact was Piglet was wishing that *he* had thought about it first.

"I shall do it," said Pooh, after waiting a little longer, "by means of a trap. And it must be a Cunning Trap, so you will have to help me, Piglet."

"Pooh," said Piglet, feeling quite happy again now, "I will." And then he said, "How shall we do it?" and Pooh said, "That's just it. How?" And then they sat down together to think it out.

Pooh's first idea was that they should dig a Very Deep Pit, and then the Heffalump would come along and fall into the Pit, and——

"Why?" said Piglet.

"Why what?" said Pooh.

"Why would he fall in?"

Pooh rubbed his nose with his paw, and said that the Heffalump might be walking along, humming a little song, and looking up at the sky, wondering if it would rain, and so he wouldn't see the Very Deep Pit until he was half-way down, when it would be too late.

Piglet said that this was a very good Trap, but supposing it were raining already?

Pooh rubbed his nose again, and said that he hadn't

thought of that. And then he brightened up, and said that, if it were raining already, the Heffalump would be looking at the sky wondering if it would *clear up,* and so he wouldn't see the Very Deep Pit until he was half-way down . . . When it would be too late.

Piglet said that, now that this point had been explained, he thought it was a Cunning Trap.

Pooh was very proud when he heard this, and he felt that the Heffalump was as good as caught already, but there was just one other thing which had to be thought about, and it was this. *Where should they dig the Very Deep Pit?*

Piglet said that the best place would be somewhere where a Heffalump was, just before he fell into it, only about a foot farther on.

"But then he would see us digging it," said Pooh.

"Not if he was looking at the sky."

"He would Suspect," said Pooh, "if he happened to look down." He thought for a long time and then added sadly, "It isn't as easy as I thought. I suppose that's why Heffalumps hardly *ever* get caught."

"That must be it," said Piglet.

They sighed and got up; and when they had taken a few gorse prickles out of themselves they sat down again; and all the time Pooh was saying to himself, "If only I could *think* of something!" For he felt sure that a Very Clever Brain could catch a Heffalump if only he knew the right way to go about it.

"Suppose," he said to Piglet, "*you* wanted to catch *me,* how would you do it?"

"Well," said Piglet, "I should do it like this. I should make a Trap, and I should put a Jar of Honey in the Trap, and you would smell it, and you would go in after it, and——"

66

"And I would go in after it," said Pooh excitedly, "only very carefully so as not to hurt myself, and I would get to the Jar of Honey, and I should lick round the edges first of all, pretending that there wasn't any more, you know, and then I should walk away and think about it a little, and then I should come back and start licking in the middle of the jar, and then——"

"Yes, well never mind about that. There you would be, and there I should catch you. Now the first thing to think of is, What do Heffalumps like? I should think acorns, shouldn't you? We'll get a lot of—I say, wake up, Pooh!"

Pooh, who had gone into a happy dream, woke up with a start, and said that Honey was a much more trappy thing than Haycorns. Piglet didn't think so; and they were just going to argue about it, when Piglet remembered that, if they put acorns in the Trap, *he* would have to find the acorns, but if they put honey, then Pooh would have to give up some of his own honey, so he said, "All right, honey then," just as Pooh remembered it too, and was going to say, "All right, haycorns."

"Honey," said Piglet to himself in a thoughtful way, as if it were now settled. *"I'll* dig the pit, while *you* go and get the honey."

"Very well," said Pooh, and he stumped off.

As soon as he got home, he went to the larder; and he stood on a chair, and took down a very large jar of honey from the top shelf. It had HUNNY written on it, but, just to make sure, he took off the paper cover and looked at it, and it *looked* just like honey. "But you never can tell," said Pooh. "I remember my uncle saying once that he had seen cheese just this

color." So he put his tongue in, and took a
large lick. "Yes," he said, "it is. No doubt
about that. And honey, I should say, right
down to the bottom of the jar. Unless, of
course," he said, "somebody put cheese in
at the bottom just for a joke. Perhaps I had
better go a *little* further . . . just in case
. . . in case Heffalumps *don't* like cheese

. . . same as me. . . . Ah!" And he gave a deep sigh. "I
was right. It *is* honey, right the way down."

Having made certain of this, he took the jar back to Piglet,
and Piglet looked up from the bottom of his Very Deep Pit,
and said, "Got it?" and Pooh said, "Yes, but it isn't quite a
full jar," and he threw it down to Piglet, and Piglet said, "No,
it isn't! Is that all you've got left?" and Pooh said "Yes." Because it was. So Piglet put the jar at the bottom of the Pit, and
climbed out, and they went off home together.

"Well, good night, Pooh," said Piglet, when they had got
to Pooh's house. "And we meet at six o'clock tomorrow morning by the Pine Trees, and see how many Heffalumps we've
got in our Trap."

"Six o'clock, Piglet. And have you got any string?"

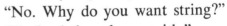

"No. Why do you want string?"

"To lead them home with."

"Oh! . . . I *think* Heffalumps come
if you whistle."

"Some do and some don't. You never
can tell with Heffalumps. Well, good
night!"

"Good night!"

And off Piglet trotted to his house

TRESPASSERS W, while Pooh made his preparations for bed.

Some hours later, just as the night was beginning to steal away, Pooh woke up suddenly with a sinking feeling. He had had that sinking feeling before, and he knew what it meant. *He was hungry.* So he went to the larder, and he stood on a chair and reached up to the top shelf, and found—nothing.

"That's funny," he thought. "I know I had a jar of honey there. A full jar, full of honey right up to the top, and it had HUNNY written on it, so that I should know it was honey. That's very funny." And then he began to wander up and down, wondering where it was and murmuring a murmur to himself. Like this:

> It's very, very funny,
> 'Cos I *know* I had some honey;
> 'Cos it had a label on,
>   Saying HUNNY.
>
> A goloptious full-up pot too,
> And I don't know where it's got to,
> No, I don't know where it's gone—
>   Well, it's funny.

He had murmured this to himself three times in a singing sort of way, when suddenly he remembered. He had put it into the Cunning Trap to catch the Heffalump.

"Bother!" said Pooh. "It all comes of trying to be kind to Heffalumps." And he got back into bed.

But he couldn't sleep. The more he tried to sleep, the more he couldn't. He tried Counting Sheep, which is sometimes a good way of getting to sleep, and, as that was no good, he tried counting Heffalumps. And that was worse. Because every Heffalump that he counted was making straight for a

pot of Pooh's honey, and *eating
it all.* For some minutes he lay
there miserably, but when the five hundred and eighty-
seventh Heffalump was licking its jaws, and saying to itself,
"Very good honey this, I don't know when I've tasted better,"
Pooh could bear it no longer. He jumped out of bed, he ran
out of the house, and he ran straight to the Six Pine Trees.

The Sun was still in bed, but there was a lightness in the
sky over the Hundred Acre Wood which seemed to show that
it was waking up and would soon be kicking off the clothes.
In the half-light the Pine Trees looked cold and lonely, and
the Very Deep Pit seemed deeper than it was, and Pooh's jar
of honey at the bottom was something mysterious, a shape
and no more. But as he got nearer to it his nose told him that
it was indeed honey, and his tongue came out and began to
polish up his mouth, ready for it.

"Bother!" said Pooh, as he got his nose inside the jar. "A
Heffalump has been eating it!" And then he thought a little
and said, "Oh, no, *I* did. I forgot."

Indeed, he had eaten most of it. But there was a little left
at the very bottom of the jar, and he pushed his head right
in, and began to lick. . . .

By and by Piglet woke up. As soon as he woke he said to
himself, "Oh!" Then he said bravely, "Yes," and then, still
more bravely, "Quite so." But he didn't feel very brave, for

70

the word which was really jiggeting about in his brain was "Heffalumps."

What was a Heffalump like?

Was it Fierce?

Did it come when you whistled? And *how* did it come?

Was it Fond of Pigs at all?

If it was Fond of Pigs, did it make any difference *what sort of Pig?*

Supposing it was Fierce with Pigs, would it make any difference *if the Pig had a grandfather called* TRESPASSERS WILLIAM?

He didn't know the answer to any of these questions . . . and he was going to see his first Heffalump in about an hour from now!

Of course Pooh would be with him, and it was much more Friendly with two. But suppose Heffalumps were Very Fierce with Pigs *and* Bears? Wouldn't it be better to pretend that he had a headache, and couldn't go up to the Six Pine Trees this morning? But then suppose that it was a very fine day, and there was no Heffalump in the trap, here he would be, in bed all the morning, simply wasting his time for nothing. What should he do?

And then he had a Clever Idea. He would go up very quietly to the Six Pine Trees now, peep very cautiously into the Trap, and see if there *was* a Heffalump there. And if there was, he would go back to bed, and if there wasn't, he wouldn't.

So off he went. At first he thought that there wouldn't be a Heffalump in the Trap, and then he thought that there would, and as he got nearer he was *sure* that there would, because he could hear it heffalumping about it like anything.

"Oh, dear, oh, dear, oh, dear!" said Piglet to himself. And

he wanted to run away. But somehow, having got so near, he felt that he must just see what a Heffalump was like. So he crept to the side of the Trap and looked in. . . .

And all the time Winnie-the-Pooh had been trying to get the honey-jar off his head. The more he shook it, the more tightly it stuck.

"Bother!" he said, inside the jar, and *"Oh, help!"* and, mostly, *"Ow!"* And he tried bumping it against things, but as he couldn't see what he was bumping it against, it didn't help him; and he tried to climb out of the Trap, but as he could see nothing but jar, and not much of that, he couldn't find his way. So at last he lifted up his head, jar and all, and made a loud, roaring noise of Sadness and Despair . . . and it was at that moment that Piglet looked down.

"Help, help!" cried Piglet, "a Heffalump, a Horrible Heffalump!" and he scampered off as hard as he could, still crying out, "Help, help, a Herrible Hoffalump! Hoff, Hoff, a Hellible Horralump! Holl, Holl, a Hoffable Hellerump!" And he didn't stop crying and scampering until he got to Christopher Robin's house.

"Whatever's the matter, Piglet?" said Christopher Robin, who was just getting up.

"Heff," said Piglet, breathing so hard that he could hardly speak, "a Heff—a Heff—a Heffalump."

"Where?"

"Up there," said Piglet, waving his paw.

"What did it look like?"

"Like—like—— It had the biggest head you ever saw, Christopher Robin. A great enormous thing, like —like nothing. A huge big—well, like

72

a—I don't know—like an enormous big nothing. Like a jar."

"Well," said Christopher Robin, putting on his shoes, "I shall go and look at it. Come on."

Piglet wasn't afraid if he had Christopher Robin with him, so off they went. . . .

"I can hear it, can't you?" said Piglet anxiously, as they got near.

"I can hear *something*," said Christopher Robin.

It was Pooh bumping his head against a tree-root he had found.

"There!" said Piglet. "Isn't it *awful?*" And he held on tight to Christopher Robin's hand.

Suddenly Christopher Robin began to laugh . . . and he laughed . . . and he laughed . . . and he laughed. And while he was still laughing—*Crash* went the Heffalump's head against the tree-root, Smash went the jar, and out came Pooh's head again. . . .

Then Piglet saw what a Foolish Piglet he had been, and he was so ashamed of himself that he ran straight off home and went to bed with a headache. But Christopher Robin and Pooh went home to breakfast together.

"Oh, Bear!" said Christopher Robin. "How I do love you!"

"So do I," said Pooh.

ONCE upon a time there was a king who was the wisest in all of the world. So wise was he that no one had ever befooled him, which is a rare thing, I can tell you. Now, this king had a daughter who was as pretty as a ripe apple, so that there was no end to the number of the lads who came asking to marry her. Every day there were two or three of them dawdling around the house, so that at last the old king grew tired of having them always about.

So he sent word far and near that whoever should befool him might have the princess and half of the kingdom to boot, for he thought that it would be a wise man indeed who could trick him. But the king also said, that whoever should try to befool him and should fail, should have a good whipping. This was to keep all foolish fellows away.

The princess was so pretty that there was no lack of lads who came to have a try for her and half of the kingdom, but every one of these went away with a sore back and no luck.

How Boots Befooled the King

BY HOWARD PYLE

Illustrated by Howard Pyle

Now, there was a man who was well off in the world, and who had three sons; the first was named Peter, and the second was named Paul. Peter and Paul thought themselves as wise as anybody in all of the world, and their father thought as they did.

As for the youngest son, he was named Boots. Nobody thought anything of him except that he was silly, for he did nothing but sit poking in the warm ashes all of the day.

74

One morning Peter spoke up and said that he was going to the town to have a try at befooling the king, for it would be a fine thing to have a princess in the family. His father did not say no, for if anybody was wise enough to befool the king, Peter was the lad.

So, after Peter had eaten a good breakfast, off he set for the town, right foot foremost. After a while he came to the king's house and—rap! tap! tap!—he knocked at the door.

Well, what did he want?

Oh! he would only like to have a try at befooling the king.

Very good; he should have his try. He was not the first one who had been there that morning, early as it was.

So Peter was shown in to the king.

"Oh, look!" said he, "yonder are three black geese out in the courtyard!"

But no, the king was not to be fooled so easily as all that. "One goose is enough to look at a time," said he; "take him away and give him a whipping!"

And so they did, and Peter went home bleating like a sheep.

One day Paul spoke up. "I should like to go and have a try for the princess, too," said he.

Well, his father did not say no, for, after all, Paul was the more clever of the two.

So off Paul went as merrily as a duck in the rain. By and by he came to the castle, and then he too was brought before the king just as Peter had been.

"Oh, look!" said he, "yonder is a crow sitting in the tree with three white stripes on his back!"

But the king was not so silly as to be fooled in that way. "Here is a Jack," said he, "who will soon have more stripes on

his back than he will like; take him away and give him his whipping!"

Then it was done as the king had said, and Paul went away home bawling like a calf.

One day up spoke Boots. "I should like to go and have a try for the pretty princess, too," said he.

At this they all stared and sniggered. What! he go where his clever brothers had failed, and had nothing to show for

76

the trying but a good beating? What had come over the lout! Here was a pretty business, to be sure! That was what they all said.

But all of this rolled away from Boots like water from a duck's back. No matter, he would like to go and have a try like the others. So he begged and begged until his father was glad to let him go to be rid of his teasing, if nothing else.

Then Boots asked if he might have the old tattered hat that hung back of the chimney.

Oh, yes, he might have that if he wanted it, for nobody with good wits was likely to wear such a thing.

So Boots took the hat, and after he had brushed the ashes from his shoes set off for the town, whistling as he went.

The first body whom he met was an old woman with a great load of earthenware pots and crocks on her shoulders.

"Good-day, mother," said Boots.

"Good-day, son," said she.

"What will you take for all of your pots and crocks?" said Boots.

"Three shillings," said she.

"I will give you five shillings if you will come and stand in front of the king's house, and do thus and so when I say this and that," said Boots.

Oh, yes! she would do that willingly enough.

So Boots and the old woman went on together, and presently came to the king's house. When they had come there, Boots sat down in front of the door and began bawling as loud as he could—"No, I will not! I will not do it, I say! No, I will not do it!"

So he kept on, bawling louder and louder until he made such a noise that, at last, the king himself came out to see what all the hubbub was about. But when Boots saw him he only bawled out louder than ever. "No, I will not! I will not do it, I say!"

"Stop! Stop!" cried the king, "what is all this about?"

"Why," said Boots, "everybody wants to buy my cap, but I will not sell it! I will not do it, I say!"

"But why should anybody want to buy such a cap as that?" said the king.

"Because," said Boots, "it is a fooling cap and the only one in all of the world."

"A fooling cap!" said the king. For he did not like to hear of such a cap as that coming into the town. "Hum-m-m-m! I should like to see you fool somebody with it. Could you fool that old body yonder with the pots and the crocks?"

"Oh, yes! that is easily enough done," said Boots, and without more ado he took off his tattered cap and blew into it. Then he put it on his head again and bawled out, "Break pots! Break pots!"

No sooner had he spoken these words than the old woman jumped up and began breaking and smashing her pots and crocks as though she had gone crazy. That was what Boots had paid her five shillings for doing, but of it the king knew nothing. "Hui!" said he to himself, "I must buy that hat from the fellow or he will fool the princess away from me for sure and certain." Then he began talking to Boots as sweetly as though he had honey in his mouth. Perhaps Boots would sell the hat to him?

Oh, no! Boots could not think of such a thing as selling his fooling cap.

Come, come; the king wanted that hat, and sooner than miss buying it he would give a whole bag of gold money for it.

At this Boots looked up and looked down, scratching his head. Well, he supposed he would have to sell the hat some time, and the king might as well have it as anybody else. But for all that he did not like parting with it.

So the king gave Boots the bag of gold, and Boots gave the king the old tattered hat, and then he went his way.

After Boots had gone the king blew into the hat and blew

into the hat, but though he blew enough breath into it to sail a big ship, he did not befool so much as a single titmouse. Then, at last, he began to see that the fooling cap was good on nobody else's head but Boot's; and he was none too pleased at that, you may be sure.

As for Boots, with his bag of gold he bought the finest clothes that were to be had in the town, and when the next morning had come he started away bright and early for the king's house. "I have come," said he, "to marry the princess, if you please."

At this the king hemmed and hawed and scratched his head. Yes, Boots had befooled him sure enough, but, after all, he could not give up the princess for such a thing as that. Still, he would give Boots another chance. Now there was the high-councillor, who was the wisest man in all of the world. Did Boots think that he could fool him also?

Oh, yes! Boots thought that it might be done.

Very well; if he could befool the high-councillor so as to bring him to the castle the next morning against his will, Boots should have the princess and the half of the kingdom; if he did not do so he should have his beating.

Then Boots went away, and the king thought that he was rid of him now for good and all.

As for the high-councillor, he was not pleased with the matter at all, for he did not like the thought of being fooled by a clever rogue, and taken here and there against his will. So when he had come home, he armed all of his servants with blunderbusses, and then waited to give Boots a welcome when he should come.

But Boots was not going to fall into any such trap as that! No indeed! Not he! The next morning he went quietly and bought a fine large meal-sack. Then he put a black wig over

80

his beautiful red hair, so that no one might know him. After that he went to the place where the high-councillor lived, and when he had come there he crawled inside of the sack, and lay just beside the door of the house.

By and by came one of the maid servants to the door, and there lay the great meal-sack with somebody in it.

"Ach!" cried she, "who is there?"

But Boots only said, "Sh-h-h-h-h!"

Then the serving maid went back into the house, and told the high-councillor that one lay outside in a great meal-sack, and that all that he said was, "Sh-h-h-h-h."

So the councillor went himself to see what it was all about. "What do you want here?" said he.

"Sh-h-h-h-h!" said Boots, "I am not to be talked to now. This is a wisdom-sack, and I am learning wisdom as fast as a drake can eat peas."

"And what wisdom have you learned?" said the councillor.

Oh! Boots had learned wisdom about everything in the world. He had learned that the clever scamp who had fooled the king yesterday was coming with seventeen tall men to take the high-councillor, willy-nilly, to the castle that morning.

When the high-councillor heard this he fell to trembling till his teeth rattled in his head. "And have you learned how I can get the better of this clever scamp?" said he.

Oh, yes! Boots had learned that easily enough.

So, good! Then if the wise man in the sack would tell the high-councillor how to escape the clever rogue, the high-councillor would give the wise man twenty dollars.

But no, that was not to be done; wisdom was not bought so cheaply as the high-councillor seemed to think.

Well, the councillor would give him a hundred dollars, then.

That was good! A hundred dollars was a hundred dollars. If the councillor would give him that much he might get into the sack himself, and then he could learn all the wisdom that he wanted, and more besides.

So Boots crawled out of the sack, and the councillor paid his hundred dollars and crawled in.

As soon as he was in all snug and safe, Boots drew the mouth of the sack together and tied it tightly. Then he flung sack, councillor, and all over his shoulder, and started away to the king's house, and anybody who met them could see with half an eye that the councillor was going against his will.

When Boots came to the king's castle he laid the councillor down in the goose-house, and then he went to the king.

When the king saw Boots again, he bit his lips with vexation. "Well," said he, "have you fooled the councillor?"

"Oh, yes!" says Boots, "I have done that."

And where was the councillor now?

Oh, Boots had just left him down in the goose-house. He was tied up safe and sound in a sack, waiting till the king should send for him.

So the councillor was sent for, and when he came the king saw at once that he had been brought against his will.

"And now may I marry the princess?" said Boots.

But the king was not willing for him to marry the princess yet; no! no! Boots must not go so fast. There was more to be done yet. If he would come tomorrow morning he might have the princess and welcome, but he would have to pick her out from among fourscore other maids just like her; did he think that he could do that?

Oh, yes! Boots thought that that might be easy enough to do.

So, good! Then come tomorrow; but he must understand that if he failed he should have a good whipping, and be sent packing from the town.

So off went Boots, and the king thought that he was rid of him now, for he had never seen the princess, and how could he pick her out from among eighty others?

But Boots was not going to give up so easily as all that! No, not he! He made a little box, and then he hunted up and down until he had caught a live mouse to put into it.

When the next morning came he started away to the king's house, taking his mouse along with him in the box.

There was the king, standing in the doorway, looking out into the street. When he saw Boots coming towards him he made a wry face. "What!" said he, "are you back again?"

Oh, yes! Boots was back again. And now if the princess was ready he would like to go and find her, for lost time was not to be gathered again like fallen apples.

So off they marched to a great room, and there stood eighty-and-one maidens, all as much alike as peas in the same dish.

Boots looked here and there, but even if he had known the princess, he could not have told her from the others. But he was ready for all that. Before any one knew what he was about, he opened the box, and out ran the little mouse among them all. Then what a screaming and a hubbub there was. Many looked as though they would have liked to swoon, but only one of them did so. As soon as the others saw what had happened, they forgot all about the mouse, and ran to her and fell to fanning her and slapping her hands and chafing her temples.

"This is the princess," said Boots.

And so it was.

After that the king could think of nothing more to set Boots to do, so he let him marry the princess as he had promised, and have half of the kingdom to boot.

That is all of this story.

Only this: It is not always the silliest one that sits kicking his feet in the ashes at home.

RAFFY was born in Africa in a thicket of bush and thorn. All day long the sun shone down on the wide plains of hard, dry earth called the veldt. But Raffy did not mind the dust and the heat. For he was a baby giraffe and the veldt is home to baby giraffes. Besides, his mother was there to lick his face and blow the dust from his brown spotted coat and make him comfortable.

At first Raffy could scarcely walk at all. His legs were wobbly and when he stood up, he had to lean against his mother to keep from falling. But he drank a great deal of milk and little by little his legs grew stronger. Soon he was walking very well indeed.

Then his mother took Raffy to the water hole, where he met ever so many animals who lived on the veldt, too. He met the hartebeest with horns straight over his eyes.

And the little gazelles who had soft tufts at the end of their tails.

The wildebeests were there, too, with their funny white beards, and the wart hog and the black-and-white-striped zebras, and the greedy water-bucks, and the tiny dik-diks with their bright brown eyes.

Close beside his mother, Raffy stood and watched them. Most interesting of all, he thought, was Longhorn, who jumped all the way across the water hole. How splendid to jump like that! Raffy wished he could do it.

Raffy and the Honkebeest

BY RITA KISSIN

Illustrated by

Charles E. Bracker

85

"Never mind," his mother said to him. "If you keep growing nicely, you will be much taller than he is. Perhaps you will be taller than I am. And I am so tall that every one of these animals must look up to me."

Raffy turned his head. Yes, his mother was the tallest animal of all. He felt very proud of her.

The next day, she began teaching Raffy his lessons. She showed him how to spread his legs apart so that he could bend down and drink without falling over. She showed him how to pull down tree branches so that he could eat the tenderest leaves. And over and over again, she told him to stay away from the forest, where fierce animals were hiding among the trees. Raffy's father went into the forest one day, just before Raffy was born, and he never came back. Raffy's mother didn't want that to happen to her baby.

So at night she made Raffy listen carefully, to the roar of the lion in the forest and the cough of the leopard and the laugh of the hyena.

"These animals are not your friends," she told him. "Always, always stay away from the forest where they live."

But of all the lessons his mother taught him, Raffy liked his running best. At first, when she started galloping across the veldt, Raffy was left far behind. But he kept on trying to catch up with her, and every day he ran just a little bit better than the day before. Sometimes, while his mother rested at noon near the water hole, Raffy would steal away and practice by himself.

"Loppity, leppity, lippity lo!
I'll be Champion Runner
Of the veldt, I know."

Raffy sang softly to himself then.

One day, to his mother's great surprise, he caught up with

86

her. In a few weeks, he was running as fast as she was. Then he began to race the other animals, the swift-footed antelopes and the gazelles. Sometimes he lost. Sometimes he won. But no matter how he came out, he was always ready to try again.

"I can beat even you now," he cried to Longhorn at the water hole one day.

Longhorn looked at Raffy, pointed his ears, cocked his head and began to run. Raffy rushed after him. On and on raced Longhorn, never glancing back. He jumped ditches and he sailed over bushes like a bird. Try as he might, Raffy could not catch up with him. For Raffy couldn't jump across ditches or sail over bushes. He had to run around them, and that took time.

"Oh, dear," thought Raffy. "I do wish I could beat him."

At that his wish came true, for Longhorn, not being as young as Raffy, had become very tired, so tired, in fact, that he slowed down and leaned against a tree, puffing hard. And Raffy, who was not tired at all, caught up with him, passed him, then turned around with a *very* pleased expression on his face.

"All right, you've beaten me," gasped Longhorn. "But I know one animal you *can't* beat—the speeding Honkebeest."

A Honkebeest! What was that? Raffy knew he had never seen one at the water hole, nor had he heard his mother mention one.

"Does Honkebeest run fast?" he now asked.

Longhorn nodded. "Faster than your mother, faster than a gazelle, faster than an antelope, faster, even, than I," he said.

"What does he look like?" asked Raffy.

"Look like!" snorted Longhorn. "He is a monster."

Then and there, Raffy made up his mind to find a Honke-beest and race him. But where was a Honkebeest to be found? Back at the water hole, Raffy counted over the animals. There were the hartebeest and the gazelle and the wart hog and the wildebeest and the water-bucks and the dik-diks—all of them. But there was not one that was new or strange, not one that looked like a monster.

When Raffy asked his mother about the Honkebeest, she said, "Of course I have seen him. Every up-to-date veldt animal knows the Honkebeest. Keep your eyes open and you'll recognize him. Besides, he goes *honk-honk.*"

So Raffy kept his eyes open for the Honkebeest. When he and his mother ran across the veldt, he looked in every direction. But day after day, no strange new animal came racing.

One afternoon, when Raffy wasn't thinking about anything special, he looked up to see an exceedingly strange creature crossing the veldt. It had a long, dark body, humped as if ready to spring. Its head had a blunt snout, and two large fiery eyes looked out above wide teeth. Its tail was made of fog. But even more strange were its flat, round legs that whirled around and around, faster than the wind, it seemed.

"I don't know what you are, but I'm going to beat you!" vowed Raffy, running pell-mell after the strange creature.

"Honk-honk!" snorted the beast at him.

And Raffy knew. This was the Honkebeest, the Honke-beest that Longhorn said Raffy must beat if he wished to be Champion.

Raffy ran faster than ever.

"Honk-honk!" snorted the creature again, leaping along and making his tail into a black cloud. *"Honk-honk!"*

"You needn't keep *honk-honking* at me!" cried Raffy.

"I'm not scared of you. And what's more, I'm going to beat you."

Off they went in a cloud of dust. On and on they sped, with Honkebeest still ahead, but with Raffy getting closer to him every minute. On and on, until they came to the water hole, where Raffy's mother was waiting for him.

"Look!" she cried to the other veldt animals. "Just look at that! Raffy is racing the Honkebeest!"

The hartebeests and the gazelles and the wildebeests and the water-bucks and the dik-diks all looked.

"I wish you well!" Cried Tommy Gazelle.

"I wish you luck!" Cried Water-buck.

"You must be quick!" Cried little Dik-dik.

Then all together they shouted, "Go to it, Raffy! Beat him! Beat the Honkebeest."

But the wart hog didn't join in. Stopping his drinking only long enough to see what the fuss was about, he waddled out still farther into the water hole, wheezing, "What a ridiculous sight! Raffy racing the Honkebeest with the whirling legs. A baby giraffe thinking he can win the championship of the veldt. It certainly makes me laugh."

Raffy was much too far away by that time to hear what the wart hog was saying. But even if he had heard it, he would not have stopped. For he was certain that he was much closer to the Honkeebeest than he had been before they passed the water hole. And Raffy was sure that in just a few moments he would pass him.

Now with another *"Honk!"* the Honkebeest went faster than ever. Raffy went faster, too. But his mouth felt dry and his tongue was thick with dust. How good it would seem to be at the water hole with his mother, putting his nose down into the clear, cool water!

But Raffy didn't turn around to go back to the water hole. He kept right on. "I must catch him and pass him. Catch him and pass him. Catch him and pass him," he said over and over to himself as he ran.

Very shortly it began to look as though Raffy really would catch up. Closer and closer he came to the snorting beast. Then, "Here I am, watch out!" cried Raffy. "I'm going to beat you any minute!"

And with that he took a bite at the tail of fog.

"Here I go," shouted Raffy. "Here I go around you."

He spoke too soon. Just then, a flying stone cut his foot and Raffy slowed down. But he didn't stop. "I'll run until I drop," he declared. "I'm not going to give up."

Now so much dust got into his eyes that he could scarcely see. Still he kept on. And once more closer and closer he came to the Honkebeest. Closer and closer until he ran past the Honkebeest's tail, past his stomach, and up beside his head.

90

Neck and neck, they raced. The sun burned down upon them. The air felt like fire. And soon Raffy was breathing so hard it seemed to him that his lungs would swell up and burst. There was a pain in his chest, too.

"But if this Honkebeest can stand it, I can," he gasped. "All I need to do now is go just a little faster and I'll be the Champion."

So Raffy did go a little faster. But the Honkebeest promptly went a little faster, too. On they sped, across the dry veldt toward the mountains.

"This is the time!" thought Raffy now. "I'll put on a little more speed and then I'll have him!"

Just then the Honkebeest turned suddenly toward a forest which Raffy hadn't noticed before. Straight toward the trees it went. Raffy caught his breath and slowed down. From every one of those trees hung moss and vines, just the place for the wild animals who were his enemies to hide. It was the dangerous jungle. Should he follow the Honkebeest into it, even though his mother had told him never, never to go in among the trees?

"Perhaps it would be all right if I went just a little way," Raffy decided. "I don't hear any lion roaring or a leopard coughing or a hyena laughing.

He started forward, then stopped suddenly. Where was the Honkebeest? Raffy looked in all directions. There wasn't a sign of the Honkebeest on the veldt or among the trees of the jungle. Only the moss and the vines waved in the wind.

"Oh, dear!" sighed Raffy sadly. "I'm sure I could have beaten him in another five minutes."

Just then he heard a sound from among the trees. Raffy jumped, ready to run away. Perhaps a lion was watching him!

It wasn't a lion. It was a friendly little monkey, coming out from behind a tree trunk and grinning at him. "I saw you from the top of the tallest tree in my jungle," she told Raffy. "It was a good race, mighty good. And if you will do as I say, you can beat the Honkebeest yet."

"How can I beat him when he's gone?" Raffy asked the friendly little monkey.

"He isn't gone. He's just out of sight," answered the monkey. "Every day he does the same thing. He comes along here and then he runs through the jungle on the road. Then he turns around and comes back another way on the veldt. Would you like to have me show you a short cut through the jungle to the place where he comes out on the veldt? Then you can race him again."

The monkey's voice was so kind that Raffy was no longer afraid. "I should like it very much, thank you," he replied. "But my mother told me never to go into the forest. The lion and the leopard and the hyena live there and we giraffes don't like them."

The monkey considered. Then she said, "Did your mother tell you not to go into the forest at all, or only if you were alone?"

Raffy couldn't remember.

"Very well then," said the monkey, "I'm sure she wouldn't object if you walked through the forest with me and my family. Come with me to my family tree and we'll get the children. When you hear the noise they make, you will realize that you are safe in the jungle!"

So Raffy followed the monkey to the family tree. High in its branches was a bed made of leaves and twigs, and over the edge of the bed three small monkeys' heads looked down.

"Come, children!" called Raffy's friend, "We're going to have fun!"

Down from the tall tree swung the little monkeys and onto Raffy's back. "It's a slide!" they shouted.

All three of them slid down Raffy's smooth back, then walked about on their hands to show Raffy how pleased they were to meet him.

"If you obey nicely, children, you may go with us," their mother told them. "This gentleman wishes to race the Honke-beest and I have promised to take him through the jungle to the place where he can find him."

"We'll obey," promised the little monkeys. "But please let us ride on the gentleman's back!"

"I don't mind," said Raffy, good-naturedly. "But you must get off when the Honkebeest comes along. I never could beat him with three monkeys on my back!"

"We'll get off when the Honkebeest comes along," promised the three little monkeys, swinging up into the family tree, then dropping down on his back. One of them rode on his tail. And off they all started together.

High above them in the trees of the jungle, monkeys were calling to each other. And here and there and everywhere, brightly colored birds flew about. It was a beautiful sight, but Raffy couldn't help being worried.

"Don't be afraid," said the mother monkey. "Those are my friends up in the trees. They will let us know if a lion or a leopard or a hyena comes along."

A hanging vine hit Raffy in the face just then, and he jumped. The three little monkeys squealed loudly.

"Besides, we are almost there," the mother monkey went on.

At that, *"Honk-honk, honk-honk,"* sounded through the jungle.

It was the Honkebeest. "Quick, this way!" cried the mother monkey. "Children, slide down at once."

In great excitement, the three little monkeys slid off Raffy's tail. And Raffy followed the mother monkey through an opening in the trees. Sure enough, there was the Honkebeest speeding across the veldt.

"Thank you!" Raffy cried hurriedly, and, like a flash,

Raffy ran after the rushing monster. He forgot about the flying stones. He paid no attention to the dust and the heat. His breath came fast and his heart beat like thunder. But he knew that this time he would win.

> *"Loppity, leppity, lippity, lo!*
> *I'll be Champion Runner*
> *Of the veldt, I know!"*

he vowed.

Once more Raffy caught up with the Honkebeest. Once more he took a bite of his tail. Once more he went past his stomach and his nose. Once more they ran neck and neck. But whenever Raffy tried to get ahead, the Honkebeest put on more speed. It was most discouraging.

Raffy was just beginning to think perhaps it would be better to wait until another day to finish the race, when suddenly the Honkebeest started to puff as though he were trying to catch his breath. Then he made queer noises in his throat, and hissed through his teeth. His body shivered and shook frightfully.

"He is trying to frighten me," thought Raffy, "and make me stop. Well, I won't. I'll show him." And taking a deep breath he ran on.

For a little way the Honkebeest raced beside Raffy. Then with a deep grunt, he stopped altogether. Like a streak, Raffy sailed on ahead and on to the water hole.

Everyone was there—Longhorn and the gazelles and the hartebeests and the zebras and the water-bucks, the little dik-diks and all the rest. In the center of them all stood Mother Giraffe, her head held high with pride.

"Hurrah! Hurrah!" they shouted when Raffy came up.

"I wished you well!" cried Tommy Gazelle.

"I brought you luck!" cried Water-buck.

"Oh, you were quick!" cried little Dik-dik.

Even lazy Wart Hog entered into the spirit of the occasion. "My young friend," he said, "I apologize for the remarks which you do not know I made. I am delighted you beat the Honkebeest and I congratulate you upon being Champion Runner of the Veldt."

"We're all glad," cried the other animals. "We all congratulate you."

"We congratulate you, too," shouted the three little monkeys and their mother, breathlessly joining the happy party.

Then each little monkey and every one of the other animals made a deep bow to Raffy, Champion Runner of them all.

ELIZABETH ELIZA had a present of a piano and she was to take lessons of the postmaster's daughter.

They decided to have the piano set across the window in the parlor, and the carters brought it in, and went away.

After they had gone the family all came in to look at the piano; but they found the carters had placed it with its back turned towards the middle of the room, standing close against the window.

How could Elizabeth Eliza open it? How could she reach the keys to play upon it?

Solomon John proposed that they should open the window, which Agamemnon could do with his long arms. Then Elizabeth Eliza should go round upon the piazza, and open the piano. Then she could have her music-stool on the piazza, and play upon the piano there.

About Elizabeth Eliza's Piano

BY LUCRETIA P. HALE

Illustrated by Harold M. Brett

So they tried this; and they all thought it was a very pretty sight to see Elizabeth Eliza playing on the piano, while she sat on the piazza, with the honeysuckle vines behind her.

It was very pleasant, too, moonlight evenings. Mr. Peterkin liked to take a doze on his sofa in the room; but the rest of the family liked to sit on the piazza. So did Elizabeth Eliza, only she had to have her back to the moon.

All this did very well through the summer; but, when the fall came, Mr. Peterkin thought the air was too cold from the open window, and the family did not want to sit out on the piazza.

97

Elizabeth Eliza practised in the mornings with her cloak on; but she was obliged to give up her music in the evenings, the family shivered so.

One day, when she was talking with the lady from Philadelphia, she spoke of this trouble.

The lady from Philadelphia looked surprised, and then said, "But why don't you turn the piano round?"

One of the little boys pertly said, "It is a square piano."

But Elizabeth Eliza went home directly, and, with the help of Agamemnon and Solomon John, turned the piano round.

"Why did we not think of that before?" said Mrs. Peterkin. "What shall we do when the lady from Philadelphia goes home again?"

98

IN the High and Far-Off Times the Elephant, O Best Beloved, had no trunk. He had only a blackish, bulgy nose, as big as a boot, that he could wriggle about from side to side; but he couldn't pick up things with it. But there was one Elephant—a new Elephant—an Elephant's Child—who was full of 'satiable curtiosity, and that means he asked ever so many questions. *And* he lived in Africa, and he filled all Africa with his 'satiable curtiosities. He asked his tall aunt, the Ostrich, why her tail-feathers grew just so, and his tall aunt the Ostrich spanked him with her hard, hard claw. He asked his tall uncle, the Giraffe, what made his skin spotty, and his tall uncle, the Giraffe, spanked him with his hard, hard hoof. And still he was full of 'satiable curtiosity! He asked his broad aunt, the Hippopotamus, why her eyes were red, and his broad aunt, the Hippopotamus, spanked him with her broad, broad hoof; and he asked his hairy uncle, the Baboon, why melons tasted just so, and his

The Elephant's Child

BY RUDYARD KIPLING

Illustrated by F. Rojankovsky

hairy uncle, the Baboon, spanked him with his hairy, hairy paw. And *still* he was full of 'satiable curtiosity! He asked questions about everything that he saw, or heard, or felt, or smelt, or touched, and all his uncles and his aunts spanked him. And still he was full of 'satiable curtiosity!

One fine morning in the middle of the Precession of the Equinoxes this 'satiable Elephant's Child asked a new fine question that he had never asked before. He asked, "What does the Crocodile have for dinner?" Then everybody said, "Hush!" in a loud and dretful tone, and they spanked him immediately and directly, without stopping, for a long time.

By and by, when that was finished, he came upon Kolokolo Bird sitting in the middle of a wait-a-bit thorn-bush, and he said, "My father has spanked me, and my mother has spanked me; all my aunts and uncles have spanked me for my 'satiable curtiosity; and *still* I want to know what the Crocodile has for dinner!"

Then Kolokolo Bird said, with a mournful cry, "Go to the banks of the great grey-green, greasy Limpopo River, all set about with fever-trees, and find out."

That very next morning, when there was nothing left of the Equinoxes, because the Precession had preceded according to precedent, this 'satiable Elephant's Child took a hundred pounds of bananas (the little short red kind), and a hundred pounds of sugar-cane (the long purple kind), and seventeen melons (the greeny-crackly kind), and said to all his dear families, "Good-bye. I am going to the great grey-green, greasy Limpopo River, all set about with fever-trees, to find out what the Crocodile has for dinner." And they all spanked him once more for luck, though he asked them most politely to stop.

Then he went away, a little warm, but not at all astonished, eating melons, and throwing the rind about, because he could not pick it up.

He went from Graham's Town to Kimberley, and from Kimberley to Khama's Country, and from Khama's Country he went east by north, eating melons all the time, till at last he came to the banks of the great grey-green, greasy Limpopo River, all set about with fever-trees, precisely as Kolokolo Bird had said.

Now you must know and understand, O Best Beloved, that till that very week, and day, and hour, and minute, this 'satiable Elephant's Child had never seen a Crocodile, and did not know what one was like. It was all his 'satiable curtiosity.

The first thing that he found was a Bi-Coloured-Python-Rock-Snake curled round a rock.

" 'Scuse me," said the Elephant's Child most politely, "but have you seen such a thing as a Crocodile in these promiscuous parts?"

"*Have* I seen a Crocodile?" said the Bi-Coloured-Python-Rock-Snake, in a voice of dretful scorn. "What will you ask me next?"

" 'Scuse me," said the Elephant's Child, "but could you kindly tell me what he has for dinner?"

Then the Bi-Coloured-Python-Rock-Snake uncoiled himself very quickly from the rock, and spanked the Elephant's Child with his scalesome, flailsome tail.

"That is odd," said the Elephant's Child, "because my father and my mother, and my uncle and my aunt, not to mention my other aunt, the Hippopotamus, and my other uncle, the Baboon, have all spanked me for my 'satiable curtiosity—and I suppose this is the same thing."

So he said good-bye very politely to the Bi-Coloured-Python-Rock-Snake, and helped to coil him up on the rock again, and went on, a little warm but not at all astonished, eating melons, and throwing the rind about, because he could not pick it up, till he trod on what he thought was a log of wood at the very edge of the great grey-green, greasy Limpopo River, all set about with fever-trees.

But it was really the Crocodile, O Best Beloved, and the Crocodile winked one eye—like this!

" 'Scuse me," said the Elephant's Child most politely, "but do you happen to have seen a Crocodile in these promiscuous parts?"

Then the Crocodile winked the other eye, and lifted half his tail out of the mud; and the Elephant's Child stepped back most politely, because he did not wish to be spanked again.

"Come hither, Little One," said the Crocodile. "Why do you ask such things?"

" 'Scuse me," said the Elephant's Child most politely, "but my father has spanked me, my mother has spanked me, not to mention my tall aunt, the Ostrich, and my tall uncle, the Giraffe, who can kick ever so hard, as well as my broad aunt, the Hippopotamus, and my hairy uncle, the Baboon, *and* including the Bi-Coloured-Python-Rock-Snake, with the scalesome, flailsome tail, just up the bank, who spanks harder than any of them; and *so,* if it's quite all the same to you, I don't want to be spanked any more."

"Come hither, Little One," said the Crocodile, "for I am the Crocodile," and he wept crocodile-tears to show it was quite true.

Then the Elephant's Child grew all breathless, and panted, and kneeled down on the bank and said, "You are the very person I have been looking for all these long days. Will you please tell me what you have for dinner?"

"Come hither, Little One," said the Crocodile, "and I'll whisper."

Then the Elephant's Child put his head down close to the Crocodile's musky, tusky mouth, and the Crocodile caught him by his little nose, which up to that very week, day, hour, and minute, had been no bigger than a boot, though much more useful.

102

"I think," said the Crocodile—and he said it between his teeth, like this—"I think to-day I will begin with Elephant's Child!"

At this, O Best Beloved, the Elephant's Child was much annoyed, and he said, speaking through his nose, like this, "Led go! You are hurtig be!"

Then the Bi-Coloured-Python-Rock-Snake scuffled down from the bank and said, "My young friend, if you do not now, immediately and instantly, pull as hard as ever you can, it is my opinion that your acquaintance in the large-pattern leather ulster" (and by this he meant the Crocodile), "will jerk you into yonder limpid stream before you can say Jack Robinson!"

This is the way Bi-Coloured-Python-Rock-Snakes always talk.

Then the Elephant's Child sat back on his little haunches, and pulled, and pulled, and pulled, and his nose began to stretch. And the Crocodile floundered into the water, making it all creamy with great sweeps of his tail, and *he* pulled, and pulled, and pulled.

And the Elephant's Child's nose kept on stretching; and the Elephant's Child spread all his little four legs and pulled, and pulled, and pulled, and his nose kept on stretching; and the Crocodile threshed his tail like an oar, and *he* pulled, and pulled, and pulled, and at each pull the Elephant's Child's nose grew longer and longer—and it hurt him hijjus!

Then the Elephant's Child felt his legs slipping, and he said through his nose, which was now nearly five feet long, "This is too butch for be!"

Then the Bi-Coloured-Python-Rock-Snake came down from the bank, and knotted himself in a double-clove-hitch round the Elephant's Child's hind legs, and said, "Rash and

inexperienced traveller, we will now seriously devote ourselves to a little high tension, because if we do not, it is my im-
pression that yonder self-propelling man-of-war with the
armor-plated upper deck" (and by this, O Best Beloved, he
meant the Crocodile), "will permanently vitiate your future
career."

That is the way all Bi-Coloured-Python-Rock-Snakes always talk.

So he pulled, and the Elephant's Child pulled, and the
Crocodile pulled; but the Elephant's Child and the Bi-
Coloured-Python-Rock-Snake pulled hardest; and at last the
Crocodile let go of the Elephant's Child's nose with a plop
that you could hear all up and down the Limpopo.

Then the Elephant's Child sat down most hard and sudden; but first he was careful to say "Thank you" to the Bi-

Coloured-Python-Rock-Snake; and next he was kind to his poor pulled nose, and wrapped it all up in cool banana leaves, and hung it in the great grey-green, greasy Limpopo to cool.

"What are you doing that for?" said the Bi-Coloured-Python-Rock-Snake.

" 'Scuse me," said the Elephant's Child, "but my nose is badly out of shape, and I am waiting for it to shrink."

"Then you will have to wait a long time," said the Bi-Coloured-Python-Rock-Snake. "Some people do not know what is good for them."

The Elephant's Child sat there for three days waiting for his nose to shrink. But it never grew any shorter, and, besides, it made him squint. For, O Best Beloved, you will see and understand that the Crocodile had pulled it out into a really truly trunk same as all Elephants have to-day.

At the end of the third day a fly came and stung him on the shoulder, and before he knew what he was doing he lifted up his trunk and hit that fly dead with the end of it.

" 'Vantage number one!" said the Bi-Coloured-Python-Rock-Snake. "You couldn't have done that with a mere-smear nose. Try and eat a little now."

Before he thought what he was doing the Elephant's Child put out his trunk and plucked a large bundle of grass, dusted it clean against his fore-legs, and stuffed it into his own mouth.

" 'Vantage number two!" said the Bi-Coloured-Python-Rock-Snake. "You couldn't have done that with a mere-smear nose. Don't you think the sun is very hot here?"

"It is!" said the Elephant's Child, and before he thought what he was doing, he schlooped up a schloop of mud from the banks of the great grey-green, greasy Limpopo, and slapped it on his head, where it made a cool schloopy-sloshy mud-cap all trickly behind his ears.

" 'Vantage number three!" said the Bi-Coloured-Python-Rock-Snake. "You couldn't have done that with a mere-smear nose. Now how do you feel about being spanked again?"

" 'Scuse me," said the Elephant's Child, "but I should not like it at all."

"How would you like to spank somebody?" said the Bi-Coloured-Python-Rock-Snake.

"I should like it very much indeed," said the Elephant's Child.

"Well," said the Bi-Coloured-Python-Rock-Snake, "you will find that new nose of yours very useful to spank people with."

106

"Thank you," said the Elephant's Child, "I'll remember that; and now I think I'll go home to all my dear families and try."

So the Elephant's Child went home across Africa frisking and whisking his trunk. When he wanted fruit to eat he pulled fruit down from a tree, instead of waiting for it to fall as he used to do. When he wanted grass he plucked grass up from the ground, instead of going on his knees as he used to do. When the flies bit him he broke off the branch of a tree and used it as a fly-whisk; and he made himself a new, cool, slushy-squshy mud-cap whenever the sun was hot. When he felt lonely walking through Africa he sang to himself down his trunk, and the noise was louder than several brass bands. He went especially out of his way to find a broad Hippopotamus (she was no relation of his), and he spanked her very hard, to make sure that the Bi-Coloured-Python-Rock-Snake had spoken the truth about his new trunk. The rest of the time he picked up the melon rinds that he had dropped on his way to the Limpopo—for he was a Tidy Pachyderm.

One dark evening he came back to all his dear families, and he coiled up his trunk and said, "How do you do?" They were very glad to see him, and immediately said, "Come here and be spanked for your 'satiable curtiosity."

"Pooh," said the Elephant's Child. "I don't think you peoples know anything about spanking; but *I* do, and I'll show you."

Then he uncurled his trunk and knocked two of his dear brothers head over heels.

"O Bananas!" said they, "where did you learn that trick, and what have you done to your nose?"

"I got a new one from the Crocodile on the banks of the great grey-green, greasy Limpopo River," said the Elephant's Child. "I asked him what he had for dinner, and he gave me this to keep."

"It looks very ugly," said his hairy uncle, the Baboon.

"It does," said the Elephant's Child. "But it's very useful," and he picked up his hairy uncle, the Baboon, by one hairy leg, and hove him into a hornet's nest.

Then that bad Elephant's Child spanked all his dear families for a long time, till they were very warm and greatly astonished. He pulled out his tall Ostrich aunt's tail-feathers; and he caught his tall uncle, the Giraffe, by the hind-leg, and dragged him through a thorn-bush; and he shouted at his broad aunt, the Hippopotamus, and blew bubbles into her ear when she was sleeping in the water after meals; but he never let any one touch Kolokolo Bird.

At last things grew so exciting that his dear families went off one by one in a hurry to the banks of the great grey-green, greasy Limpopo River, all set about with fever-trees, to borrow new noses from the Crocodile. When they came back nobody spanked anybody any more; and ever since that day, O Best Beloved, all the Elephants you will ever see, besides all those that you won't, have trunks precisely like the trunk of the 'satiable Elephant's Child.

AMONG all those mortals who grew so wise that they learned the secrets of the gods, none was more cunning than Daedalus.

He once built for King Minos of Crete a wonderful Labyrinth of winding ways so cunningly tangled up and twisted around that, once inside, you could never find your way out again without a magic clue. But the king's favor veered with the wind, and one day he had his master architect imprisoned in a tower. Daedalus managed to escape from his cell; but it seemed impossible to leave the island, since every ship that came or went was well guarded by order of the king.

At length, watching the seagulls in the air—the only creatures that were sure of liberty—he thought of a plan for himself and his young son Icarus, who was captive with him.

Little by little, he gathered a store of feathers great and small. He fastened these together with thread, molded them in with wax, and so fashioned two great wings like those of a bird. When they were done, Daedalus fitted them to his own shoulders, and after one or two efforts, he found that by waving his arms he could winnow the air and cleave it, as a swimmer does the sea. He held himself aloft, wavered this way and that with the wind, and at last, like a great fledgling, he learned to fly.

Without delay, he fell to work on a pair of wings for the boy Icarus, and taught him carefully how to use them, bidding him beware of rash adventures among the stars. "Re-

Icarus and Daedalus

RETOLD BY
JOSEPHINE PEABODY

Illustrated by Roger Duvoisin

109

member," said the father, "never to fly very low or very high, for the fogs about the earth would weigh you down, but the blaze of the sun will surely melt your feathers apart if you go too near."

For Icarus, these cautions went in at one ear and out by the other. Who could remember to be careful when he was to fly for the first time? Are birds careful? Not they! And not an idea remained in the boy's head but the one joy of escape.

The day came, and the fair wind that was to set them free. The father bird put on his wings, and, while the light urged them to be gone, he waited to see that all was well with Icarus, for the two could not fly hand in hand. Up they rose, the boy after his father. The hateful ground of Crete sank beneath them; and the country folk, who caught a glimpse of them when they were high above the tree-tops, took it for a vision of the gods—Apollo, perhaps, with Cupid after him.

At first there was a terror in the joy. The wide vacancy of the air dazed him—a glance downward made their brains reel. But when a great wind filled their wings, and Icarus felt himself sustained, like a halcyon-bird in the hollow of a wave, like a child up-lifted by his mother, he forgot everything in the world but joy. He forgot Crete and the other islands that he had passed over: he saw but vaguely that wingéd thing in the distance before him that was his father Daedalus. He longed for one draught of flight to quench the thirst of his captivity: he stretched out his arms to the sky and made towards the highest heavens.

Alas for him! Warmer and warmer grew the air. Those arms, that had seemed to uphold him, relaxed. His wings wavered, drooped. He fluttered his young hands vainly—he was falling—and in that terror he remembered. The heat of

110

the sun had melted the wax from his wings; the feathers were falling, one by one, like snowflakes; and there was none to help.

He fell like a leaf tossed down the wind, down, down, with one cry that overtook Daedalus far away. When he returned and sought high and low for the poor boy, he saw nothing but the bird-like feathers afloat on the water, and he knew that Icarus was drowned.

The nearest island he named Icaria, in memory of the child; but he, in heavy grief, went to the temple of Apollo in Sicily, and there hung up his wings as an offering. Never again did he attempt to fly.

IT was the Eve of St. Stephen, and Teig sat alone by his fire with naught in his cupboard but a pinch of tea and a bare mixing of meal, and a heart inside of him as soft and warm as the ice on the water-bucket outside the door. The turf was near burnt on the hearth—a handful of golden cinders left, just; and Teig took to counting them greedily on his fingers.

"There's one, two, three, an' four an' five," he laughed. "Faith, there be more bits o' real gold hid undther the loose clay in the corner."

It was the truth; and it was the scraping and scrooching for the last piece that had left Teig's cupboard bare of a Christmas dinner.

"Gold is betther nor eatin' an' dthrinkin'. An' if ye have naught to give, there'll be naught asked of ye." And he laughed again.

He was thinking of the neighbors, and the doles of food and piggins of milk that would pass

The Voyage of the Wee Red Cap

BY RUTH SAWYER

Illustrated by Susanne Suba

over their thresholds that night to the vagabonds and paupers who were sure to come begging. And on the heels of that thought followed another: who would be giving old Shawn his dinner? Shawn lived a stone's throw from Teig, alone, in a wee tumbled-in cabin; and for a score of years past Teig had stood on the door-step every Christmas Eve, and, making a hollow of his two hands, had called across the road:

"Hey, there, Shawn, will ye come over for a sup?" And

Shawn had reached for his crutches—there being but one leg to him—and had come.

"Faith," said Teig, trying another laugh, "Shawn can fast for the once; 'twill be all the same in a month's time." And he fell to thinking of the gold again.

A knock came at the door. Teig pulled himself down in his chair where the shadow would cover him, and held his tongue.

"Teig, Teig!" It was the Widow O'Donnelly's voice. "If ye are there, open your door. I have not got the pay for the spriggin' this month, an' the childher are needin' food."

But Teig put the leash on his tongue, and never stirred till he heard the tramp of her feet going on to the next cabin. Then he saw to it that the door was tight-barred. Another knock came, and it was a stranger's voice this time:

"The other cabins are filled; not one but has its hearth crowded; will ye take us in—the two of us? The wind bites mortal sharp; not a morsel o' food have we tasted this day. Masther, will ye take us in?"

But Teig sat on, a-holding his tongue; and the tramp of the strangers' feet passed down the road. Others took their place—small feet, running. It was the miller's wee Cassie, and she called out as she went by:

"Old Shawn's watchin' for ye. Ye'll not be forgettin' him, will ye, Teig?"

And then the child broke into a song, sweet and clear, as she passed down the road:

"Listen all ye, 'tis the Feast o' St. Stephen,
Mind that ye keep it, this holy even.
Open your door an' greet ye the stranger,
For ye mind that the wee Lord had naught but a manger.
                    Mhuire as truagh!

> *"Feed ye the hungry an' rest ye the weary,*
> *This ye must do for the sake of Our Mary.*
> *'Tis well that ye mind—ye who sit by the fire—*
> *That the Lord He was born in a dark and cold byre.*
> > *Mhuire as truagh!"*

Teig put his finger deep in his ears. "A million murdthering curses on them that won't let me be! Can't a man try to keep what is his without bein' pesthered by them that has only idled an' wasted their days?"

And then the strange thing happened: hundreds and hundreds of wee lights began dancing outside the window, making the room bright; the hands of the clock began chasing each other round the dial, and the bolt of the door drew itself out. Slowly, without a creak or a cringe, the door opened, and in there trooped a crowd of Good People. Their wee green cloaks were folded close about them, and each carried a rush candle.

114

Teig was filled with a great wonderment, entirely, when he saw the fairies, but when they saw him they laughed.

"We are takin' the loan o' your cabin this night, Teig," said they. "Ye are the only man hereabouts with an empty hearth, an' we're needin' one."

Without saying more, they bustled about the room making ready. They lengthened out the table and spread and set it; more of the Good People trooped in, bringing stools and food and drink. The pipers came last, and they sat themselves around the chimneypiece a-blowing their chanters and trying the drones. The feasting began and the pipers played, and never had Teig seen such a sight in his life. Suddenly a wee man sang out:

"Clip, clap, clip, clap, I wish I had my wee red cap!"

And out of the air there tumbled the neatest cap Teig ever laid his two eyes on. The wee man clapped it on his head, crying:

"I wish I was in Spain!" and—whist!—up the chimney he went, and away out of sight!

It happened just as I am telling it. Another wee man called for his cap, and away he went after the first. And then another and another until the room was empty and Teig sat alone again.

"By my soul," said Teig, "I'd like to thravel that way myself! It's grand savin' of tickets an' baggage; an' ye get to a place before ye've had time to change your mind. Faith, there is no harm done if I thry it."

So he sang the fairies' rhyme and out of the air dropped a wee cap for him. For a moment the wonder had him, but the next he was clapping the cap on his head, crying:

"Spain!"

Then—whist!—up the chimney he went after the fairies,

and before he had time to let out his breath he was standing in the middle of Spain, and strangeness all about him.

He was in a great city. The doorways of the houses were hung with flowers and the air was warm and sweet with the smell of them. Torches burned along the streets, sweetmeat-sellers went about crying their wares, and on the steps of a cathedral crouched a crowd of beggars.

"What's the meanin' o' that?" asked Teig of one of the fairies.

"They are waiting for those that are hearing Mass. When they come out, they give half of what they have to those that have nothing, so on this night of all the year there shall be no hunger and no cold."

And then far down the street came the sound of a child's voice, singing:

> *"Listen all ye, 'tis the Feast o' St. Stephen,*
> *Mind that ye keep it, this holy even."*

Suba

"Curse it!" said Teig; "can a song fly afther ye?" And then he heard the fairies cry, "Holland!" and he cried "Holland!" too.

In one leap he was over France, and in another over Belgium, and with the third he was standing by long ditches of water frozen fast, and over them glided hundreds upon hundreds of lads and maids. Outside each door stood a wee wooden shoe, empty. Teig saw scores of them as he looked down the ditch of a street.

"What is the meanin' o' those shoes?" he asked the fairies.

"Ye poor lad!" answered the wee man next to him; "are ye not knowing anything? This is the Gift Night of the year, when every man gives to his neighbor."

A child came to the window of one of the houses, and in her hand was a lighted candle. She was singing as she put the light down close to the glass, and Teig caught the words:

"Open your door an' greet ye the stranger—
For ye mind that the wee Lord had naught but a manger.
Mhuire as truagh!"

" 'Tis the devil's work!" cried Teig, and he set the red cap more firmly on his head.

"I'm for another country."

I cannot be telling you a half of the adventures Teig had that night, nor half the sights that he saw. But he passed by fields that held sheaves of grain for the birds, and door-steps that held bowls of porridge for the wee creatures. He saw lighted trees, sparkling and heavy with gifts; and he stood outside the churches and watched the crowds pass in, bearing gifts to the Holy Mother and Child.

At last the fairies straightened their caps and cried, "Now for the great hall in the King of England's palace!"

117

Whist!—and away they went, and Teig after them; and the first thing he knew he was in London, not an arm's-length from the King's throne. It was a grander sight than he had seen in any other country. The hall was filled entirely with lords and ladies; and the great doors were open for the poor and the homeless to come in and warm themselves by the King's fire and feast from the King's table. And many a hungry soul did the King serve with his own hands.

Those that had anything to give gave it in return. It might be a bit of music played on a harp or a pipe, or it might be a dance or a song; but more often it was a wish, just, for good luck and safe-keeping.

Teig was so taken up with the watching that he never heard the fairies when they wished themselves off; moreover, he never saw the wee girl that was fed, and went laughing away. But he heard a bit of her song as she passed through the door:

"Feed ye the hungry an' rest ye the weary,
This ye must do for the sake of Our Mary."

Then the anger had Teig. "I'll stop your pestherin' tongue, once an' for all time!" and, catching the cap from his head, he threw it after her.

No sooner was the cap gone than every soul in the hall saw him. The next moment they were about him, catching at his coat and crying:

"Where is he from? What does he here? Bring him before the King!" And Teig was dragged along by a hundred hands to the throne where the King sat.

"He was stealing food," cried one.

"He was stealing the King's jewels," cried another.

"He looks evil," cried a third. "Kill him!"

118

And in a moment all the voices took it up and the hall rang with, "Aye, kill him, kill him!"

Teig's legs took to trembling, and fear put the leash on his tongue; but after a long silence he managed to whisper:

"I have done evil to no one, no one!"

"Maybe," said the King. "But have ye done good? Come, tell us, have ye given aught to any one this night? If ye have, we will pardon ye."

Not a word could Teig say—fear tightened the leash— for he was knowing full well there was no good to him that night.

"Then ye must die," said the King. "Will ye try hanging or beheading?"

"Hanging, please, your Majesty," said Teig.

The guards came rushing up and carried him off. But as he was crossing the threshold of the hall a thought sprang at him and held him.

"Your Majesty," he called after him, "will ye grant me a last request?"

"I will," said the King.

"Thank ye. There's a wee red cap that I'm mortal fond of,

119

and I lost it a while ago; if I could be hung with it on, I would hang a deal more comfortable."

The cap was found and brought to Teig.

"Clip, clap, clip, clap, for my wee red cap. I wish I was home," he sang.

Up and over the heads of the dumfounded guard he flew, and—whist!—and away out of sight. When he opened his eyes again, he was sitting close by his own hearth, with the fire burnt low. The hands of the clock were still, the bolt was fixed firm in the door. The fairies' lights were gone, and the only bright thing was the candle burning in old Shawn's cabin across the road.

A running of feet sounded outside, and then the snatch of a song:

> "'Tis well that ye mind, ye who sit by the fire,
> That the Lord He was born in a dark and cold byre.
> > Mhuire as truagh!"

"Wait ye, whoever ye are!" and Teig was away to the corner, digging fast at the loose clay, as a terrier digs at a bone. He filled his hands full of the shining gold, then hurried to the door, unbarring it.

The miller's wee Cassie stood there, peering at him out of the darkness.

"Take those to the Widow O'Donnelly, do ye hear? And take the rest to the store. Ye tell Jamie to bring up all that he has that is eatable an' dhrinkable; an' to the neighbors ye say, 'Teig's keepin' the feast this night.' Hurry now!"

Teig stopped a moment on the threshold until the tramp of her feet had died away; then he made a hollow of his two hands and called across the road:

"Hey there, Shawn, will ye come over for a sup?"

120

SHE was a witch, she was very old, and she was always hungry, and she lived long ago near a forest where now is Uruguay, and just in the corner where Brazil and Argentina touch. They were the days when mighty beasts moved in the marshes and when strange creatures with wings like bats flew in the air. There were also great worms then, so strong that they bored through mountains and rocks as an ordinary worm makes its way through clay. The size and the strength of the old witch may be guessed when you know that she once caught one of the giant worms and killed it for the sake of the stone in its head.

And there is this about the stone —it is green in colour and shaped like an arrow-head a little blunted, and precious for those who know the secret, because he who has one may fly through the air between sunrise and sunset, but never in the night.

The Hungry Old Witch

BY CHARLES FINGER

Illustrated by Marvin Fuller

The old witch had another secret thing. It was a powder, and the knowledge of how to make it was hers alone and is now lost. All that is known of it is that it was made from the dried bodies of tree-frogs mixed with goat's milk. With it she could, by sprinkling a little of it where wanted, make things grow wonderfully. She could also turn plants into animals with it, or change vines into serpents, thorn-bushes into foxes, little leaves into ants. Living creatures she also changed, turning cats into jaguars, lizards into alligators, and bats into horrible flying things.

121

This old witch had lived for hundreds of years, so long indeed that the memory of men did not know a time when she was not, and fathers and grandfathers and great grandfathers all had the same tale to tell of how she had always devoured cattle and pigs and goats, making no account at all of carrying off in one night all the animals of a village. To be sure, some had tried to fight her by shooting arrows, but it was of no use, for by her magic the shafts were bent into a shape like a letter V as soon as they touched her. So in time it came about that men would put outside the village in a corral one half of what they had raised in a year, letting the old witch take it, hoping that thus she would leave them in peace.

At last there grew up a lad, a sober fellow of courage, who said little and thought much, and he refused to take animals to the corral when the time came for the old witch to visit that place.

When the people asked him his reason for refusing, he said that he had had a dream in which he saw himself as a bird in a cage, but when he had been there a little while a sweet climbing vine had grown up about the cage and on this vine was a white flower which twisted its way in between the bars. Then, as he looked at it, the flower changed to a smiling maiden who held a golden key in her hand. This key she had given to him and with it he had opened the door of the cage. So, he went on to say, both he and the maiden had gone away. What the end of the dream was he did not know, for at that point he had wakened with the sound of singing and music in his ears, from which he judged that all turned out well, though he had not seen the end of it.

Because of this dream and what it might betoken he said that he would not put anything in the corral for the old

122

witch, but instead would venture forth and seek her out, to the end that the land might be free from her witcheries and evil work. Nor could any persuade him to the contrary.

"It is not right," he said, "that we should give away for nothing that which we have grown and tended and learned to love, nor is it right that we should feed and fatten the evil thing that destroys us."

So the wise men of that place named the lad by a word which means Stout Heart, and because he was loved by all, many trembled and turned pale when the morning came on which he took his lance and alone went off into the forest, ready for whatever might befall.

For three days Stout Heart walked, and at last came to a place all grassy and flowery, where he sat down by the side of a lake under a tree. He was tired, for he had walked far that day and found that slumber began to overtake him. That was well enough, for he was used to sleep under the bare heavens, but with his slumber came confused dreams of harmful things which he seemed to see coming out of the ground, so he climbed into the tree, where he found a resting-place among the branches and was soon asleep.

While he slept there came to the side of the lake the old witch, who cast her basket-net into the water and began to fish, and as she fished she sang in a croaking and harsh voice this:

> "*Things in the air,*
> *Things in the water—*
> *Nothing is fair,*
> *So come to the slaughter.*"

They were not the words, but that is what the words meant. But, unpleasant as was the song, yet it worked a kind of charm, and things came to her, so that her basket-net was filled again and again. The fish she cast into a kind of wicker cage, of which she had several.

Soon the croaking song chased sleep from the eyes of Stout Heart, and looking down he saw the wrinkled crone and the great pile of fish that she had cast on the bank, and his heart was grieved for two things—one that there was such waste of good life, the other that he had left his spear hidden in the grass. He grieved too, a little, because he knew that on account of his long walk he was weak from hunger and thirst. So there seemed little that could be done and he sat very still, trusting that until he was better prepared for action the old witch would not see him.

But all his stillness was of no avail. Looking at the shadow of the tree as it lay upon the surface of the water, she saw the lad's shadow. Then she looked up and saw him. Had she had her magic green stone with her, things would have been far different and this tale all the shorter. But not having it and being quite unable to climb trees, she said:

"You are faint and hungry. Come down, come down, good lad, for I have much here that is good to eat."

Hearing that, Stout Heart laughed, knowing that she was not to be trusted, and he told her that he was very well indeed where he was. So she tried another trick, spreading on the grass fruits and berries, and saying in a wheedling voice:

"Come, son, eat with me. I do not like to eat alone. Here are fresh fruits and here is honey. Come down that I may talk with you and treat you as a son, for I am very lonesome."

But Stout Heart still laughed at her, although, to be sure, he was a lad of great appetite and his hungriness increased in him.

"Have you any other trap to set for me?" he asked.

124

Hearing that, the witch fell into a black and terrible rage, dancing about and gnashing her teeth, frothing at the mouth and hooking her long nails at him like a cat, and the sight of her was very horrible, but the lad kept his heart up and was well content with his place in the tree, the more as he saw her great strength. For in her rage she plucked a great rock the size of a man's body from the earth where it was sunk deep, and cast it at the tree with such force that the tree shook from root to tip.

For a moment the old witch stood with knit brows, then she went on her hands and knees and fell to gathering up blades of grass until she had a little heap. All the time she was cursing and groaning, grumbling and snarling like a cat. When she had gathered enough grass she stood up and began to sprinkle a grayish powder over the grass heap, and as she did this she talked mumblingly, saying:

"Creep and crawl—creep and crawl!
Up the tree-trunk, on the branch.
Creep and crawl—creep and crawl!
Over leaf and over twig.
Seek and find the living thing.
Pinch him, bite him, torture him.
Creep and crawl—creep and crawl!
Make him drop like rotting fruit."

So she went on, moving about in a little circle and sprinkling the powder over the grass. Presently the pile of grass began to move as if it hid some living thing, and soon the grass blades became smaller, rounded themselves, and turned brown. Then from them shot out fine hair-like points which became legs, and so each separate leaf turned to an ant. To the tree they scurried and up the trunk they swarmed, a

125

little army marching over every leaf and twig until the green became brown, and louder and louder the old witch screamed, waving her arms the while:

"Creep and crawl—creep and crawl!
Up the tree-trunk, on the branch.
Creep and crawl—creep and crawl!"

The nearer to Stout Heart that they came, the louder she shrieked, leaping about and waving her long-taloned hands as she ordered:

"Seek and find the living thing."

Then Stout Heart knew that trouble was brewing indeed, for against so many enemies there was no fighting. For a time he avoided them, but for a time only, and that by going higher and higher in the tree, crawling along the branch that hung over the lake, but nearer and nearer the ants came, and louder she bade them to

"Pinch him, bite him, torture him."

At last there was nothing for it but to drop out of the tree, for he had been hanging to the end of a branch and the ants were already swarming over his hands and some running down his arms. So he let go his hold and went into the lake with a splash, down out of the sunshine and into the cool green-blue of the waters. He swam a little, trying to get out of the way before coming up, but had to put his head out soon to get a breath. Then suddenly he seemed to be in the middle of something that was moving about strangely, and it was with a sudden leaping of the heart that he found himself in the old witch's basket-net being drawn ashore. To be sure, he struggled and tried to escape, but it was of no use. What with

126

her magic and her strength he was no more in her hands than
is a little fish in the hands of a man. He was all mixed up
with other lake things, with fish and with scum, with water-
beetles and sticky weed, with mud and with wriggling creatures, and presently he found himself toppled head foremost
into a basket, all dazed and weak. It was dark there, but by
the bumping he knew that he was being carried somewhere.

Soon he was tumbled into an evil-smelling place and must
have fallen into a trance, or slept. Again, he may not have
known what passed because of the old witch's enchantments,
for when he came to himself he did not know whether he had
been there for a long time or a little. But soon he made out
that he was in a stone house and through a small hole in the
wall saw that the place where the house stood was bare of
grass and full of great gray rocks, and he remembered his
dream and thought that it was all very unlike what had
really happened.

But in that he was not altogether right, for while he was
in no cage and no twining vine with glorious flower was there,
yet there was something else. For after a little while a door
opened, and he saw standing in a light that nearly blinded

127

him with its brightness, a maiden full of winning grace, and light and slender, who stretched out her hand to him and led him out of the dark into a great hall of stone with a vast fireplace. Then having heard his story, which brought tears to her blue eyes, she opened a lattice and showed him a little room where he might hide.

"For," said she, "I also was brought to this place long ago, and when I came the old witch killed one who was her slave before me. But before she died she told me the story of the green stone which the witch has, and also how the magic powders were used. Since then I have been here alone and have been her slave. But now she will kill me and will keep you for her servant until she tires of you, when she will catch another. And so it has been for many, many years, and each one that dies has told the power of the green stone to the other, though none had dared to use it."

Now hearing all that, Stout Heart was all for running away at once and taking the maiden from that dreadful place, but just as he opened his mouth to speak there came to their ears the voice of the old witch.

"Hide then," said the maiden, "and all may yet go well. For I must go to get the green stone by means of which we may fly. With you I will dare. Alone I was afraid to venture."

Even then he hesitated and did not wish to hide, but she thrust him into a little room and closed the door. Through the wall he heard the witch enter and throw a pile of wood on the hearth.

"I have a new prize," said the ogress. "You I have fattened long enough and now you must be my meal. One slave at a time is enough for me, and the lad will do. Go then, fetch pepper and salt, red pepper and black, and see to it that you lose no time, for I am hungry and cannot wait."

128

The girl went into another room and the witch fell on her knees and began to build a roaring fire. Soon the maiden re-entered, but running lightly, and as she passed the old woman she cast on her some of the magic powder which she had brought instead of salt and pepper. The hag had no idea that it was the powder that the girl had thrown, and thinking that she had been careless with the salt and pepper began to scold her, then getting to her feet took her by the hair, opened the door of the little room in which Stout Heart was, and little knowing that the lad was there cast her in, screaming:

"Stay there, useless one, until I am ready to roast you."

The maiden thrust the green stone into the hands of Stout Heart and at once they flew through the window and out under the arch of the sky. As for the old witch, the powder did its work and she began to swell so that she could not pass out of any of the doors. But presently the boy and girl, from a height at which they could see below them the narrow valley and the witch's house, saw that the old hag was struggling to get out by way of the roof.

The two lost no time then. They flew swift and high. But swift too was the witch. Her growing had finished and out over the top of the house she burst, and seeing the escaping pair, began to run in the direction they had taken.

So there was much speeding both in the air and on the earth, and unlucky it was for the two that the green stone allowed those who carried it to fly only in the daytime. All this the maiden told Stout Heart as they flew. The old witch well remembered that at night there was no power in the flying stone and was gleeful in her wicked old heart as she watched the sun and the lengthening shadows. So she kept on with giant strides and leapings, and going at such a rate that she was always very nigh under the two in the air. No deer, no

huanaco could have bounded lighter over the ground than
she did, and no ostrich could have moved swifter.

When the sun began to drop in the western sky, and he
and she were looking at one another with concern as they flew,
the maiden bethought her of a plan, and scattering some of
the magic powder on the earth she rejoiced to see that the
leaves on which the powder fell turned into rabbits. The sight
of that the witch could not resist, and she stopped a moment
to catch some of the little animals and swallow them, so a little time was won for the fliers.

But the hungry old witch soon went on and regained the
time she had lost and was under them again, running as fast
as ever. So more powder was scattered, this time on some
thorn-bushes, which changed to foxes. Again the old woman
stopped to eat and the two gained a little. But the sun was
lower and they found themselves dropping ever nearer to the
earth, flying indeed but little higher than the tree-tops, and,
as they saw, the old witch in her leaps lacked but little of
touching them.

Ahead of them was the lake in which Stout Heart had

130

been caught, the waters red as blood with the light of the western sky, but the power of the stone was failing with the waning day, and of the powder they had but a small handful left. As for the witch, so near was she that they could hear her breathing, could almost imagine that they felt her terrible claws in their garments.

On the bank of the lake the last handful of the magic powder was cast, and they saw the grass turn to ants and the stones to great turtles as they passed over the water, but so low that their feet almost touched the surface of the lake. The power of the stone was growing weak.

The old witch, seeing the turtles, stopped to swallow them, shells and heads, and that gave the youth and maiden time enough to reach the opposite shore, where the power of the stone was quite exhausted as the sun touched the rim of the earth. The gentle maiden clung to Stout Heart in great fear then as they saw the old witch plunge into the lake, for she could travel on water as fast as she could on land. Indeed, the fearful old woman cut through the waters so swiftly that a great wave leaped up on either side of her, and it was clear that before the sun had gone she would have her claws in the two friends.

But when she was in the middle of the lake the weight of the turtles she had swallowed began to bear her down. In vain she struggled, making a great uproar and lashing her hands and feet so furiously that the water became hot and a great steam rose up. Her force was spent and the turtles were like a great stone within her, so she sank beneath the water, and was seen no more.

Great was the joy of the people when Stout Heart brought the maiden to his home, for she became his wife and was loved by all there as the fairest woman among them.

131

IT was so lovely in the country—it was summer! The wheat was yellow, the oats were green, the hay was stacked in the green meadows, and down there the stork went tiptoeing on his red legs, jabbering Egyptian, a language his mother had taught him. Round about the fields and meadows were great forests, and in the midst of those forests lay deep lakes. Yes, it was indeed lovely in the country! Bathed in sunshine there stood an old manor house, surrounded by a deep moat, and from the walls down to the water's edge the bank was covered with great wild rhubarb

leaves so high that little children could stand upright under the biggest of them. The place was as much of a wilderness as the densest wood, and there sat a duck on her nest; she was busy hatching her ducklings, but she was almost tired of it, because sitting is such tedious business, and she had very few callers. The other ducks thought it more fun to swim about in the moat than

The Ugly Duckling

BY HANS CHRISTIAN ANDERSEN

Illustrated by Richard Benne

to come and have a gossip with her under a wild rhubarb leaf.

At last one eggshell after another began to crack open. "Cheep, cheep!" All the yolks had come to life and were sticking out their heads.

"Quack, quack," said the duck, and all her ducklings came scurrying out as fast as they could, looking about under the green leaves, and their mother let them look as much as they liked, because green is good for the eyes

"How big the world is!" said all the ducklings, for they felt much more comfortable now than when they were lying in the egg.

"Do you imagine this is the whole of the world?" asked their mother. "It goes far beyond the other side of the garden, right into the Rector's field, but I've never been there yet. I hope you're all here, she went on, and hoisted herself up. "No, I haven't got all of you even now; the biggest egg is still there. I wonder how much longer it will take! I'm getting rather bored with the whole thing." And she squatted down again on the nest.

"Well, how are you getting on?" asked an old duck who came to call on her.

"That last egg is taking an awfully long time," said the brooding duck. "It won't break; but let me show you the others, they're the sweetest ducklings I've ever seen. They are all exactly like their father; the scamp—he never comes to see me!"

"Let me look at the egg that won't break," said the old duck. "You may be sure it's a turkey's egg. I was fooled like that once, and the trouble and bother I had with those youngsters, because they were actually afraid of the water! I simply couldn't get them to go in! I quacked at them and I snapped at them, but it was no use. Let me see the egg—of course it's a turkey's egg; leave it alone, and teach the other children to swim."

"Oh, well, if I've taken so much trouble I may just as well sit a little longer," said the duck.

"Please yourself," said the old duck, and she waddled off.

At last the big egg cracked. "Cheep, cheep!" said the youngster, scrambling out; he was so big and ugly! The duck looked at him: "What a frightfully big duckling that one is," she said. "None of the others looked like that! Could he pos-

133

sibly be a turkey chick? We'll soon find out; he'll have to go into the water, even if I have to kick him in myself!"

The next day the weather was simply glorious; the sun shone on all the wild rhubarb plants. Mother Duck appeared with her family down by the moat. Splash! There she was in the water! "Quack, quack," she said, and one duckling after another plumped in. The water closed over their heads, but they were up again in a second and floated beautifully. Their legs worked of their own accord; they were all out in the water now, and even the ugly gray creature was swimming along with them.

"That's no turkey!" she said. "Look how nicely he uses his legs, and how straight he holds himself! He's my own flesh and blood, I tell you. He isn't really so bad when you take a good look at him. Quack, quack—come along with me, I'll bring you out into the world and introduce you to the duck-yard, but keep close to me or you may get stepped on, and look out for the cat!"

So they made their entrance into the duckyard. What a pandemonium there was! Two families were quarreling over an eel's head; but in the end the cat got it.

"There you are, that's the way of the world!" said Mother Duck, licking her lips, for she did so want the eel's head herself. "Now use your legs," she said. "Move about briskly and curtsey with your necks to the old duck over there; she is the most aristocratic person here, and of Spanish blood, that's why she is so stout; and be sure to observe that red rag round her leg. It's a great distinction, and the highest honor that can be bestowed upon a duck: it means that her owner wishes to keep her, and that she is to be specially noticed by man and beast. Now hurry! Don't turn your toes in; a well-brought-up duckling turns his toes out just as father and mother do—like

134

that. That's right! Now make a deep curtesy with your necks and say, 'Quack, quack!' "

And they did as they were told; but the other ducks all round about looked at them and said out loud, "There now! have we got to have that crowd too? As if there weren't enough of us already; and ugh! what a dreadful-looking creature that duckling is! We won't put up with him." And immediately a duck rushed at him and bit him in the neck.

"Leave him alone," said the mother. "He's not bothering any of you."

"I know," said the duck who had bitten him, "but he's too big and odd. What he wants is a good smacking."

"Those are pretty children you've got, Mother," said the old duck with the rag round her leg. "They are all nice-looking except that one—he didn't turn out so well. I wish he could be made all over again!"

"That can't be done, Your Grace," said Mother Duck. "He's not handsome, but he's as good as gold, and he swims as well as any of the others, I daresay even a little better. I expect his looks will improve, or perhaps in time his size won't be so noticeable. He was in the egg too long, that's why he isn't properly shaped." And she pecked his neck and brushed up the little man. "As it happens he's a drake," she added, "so it doesn't matter quite so much. I think he'll be a strong fellow, and I'm sure he'll make his mark in the world."

"The other ducklings are lovely," said the old duck. "Make yourselves at home, and if you find an eel's head— you may bring it to me."

So at once they felt at home.

But the poor duckling who was the last to be hatched, and who looked so ugly, was bitten and buffeted about and made fun of both by the ducks and the hens. "He's too big!" they all

135

said. And the turkey-cock, who was born with spurs and consequently thought he was an Emperor, blew himself up like a ship in full sail and made for him, gobbling and gabbling till his wattles were quite purple. The poor duckling did not know where to turn; he was so miserable because of his ugliness, and because he was the butt of the whole barnyard.

And so it went on all the first day, and after that matters grew worse and worse. The poor duckling was chased about by everyone; his own brothers and sisters were downright nasty to him and always said, "I hope the cat gets you, you skinny bag of bones!" And even his mother said, "I wish you were miles away!" And the ducks bit him and the hens pecked him, and the girl who fed them kicked him with her foot.

So, half running and half flying, he got over the fence.

The little birds in the bushes rose up in alarm. "That's because I'm so ugly," thought the duckling, and closed his eyes, but he kept on running, and finally came out into the great marsh where the wild ducks lived. There he lay the whole night long, tired and downhearted.

In the morning the wild ducks flew up and looked at their new companion. "What sort of a fellow are you?" they asked, and the duckling turned in all directions bowing to everybody as nicely as he could.

"You're appallingly ugly!" said the wild ducks, "but why should we care so long as you don't marry into our family?" Poor thing! as if he had any thought of marrying! All he wanted to do was to lie among the reeds, and to drink a little marsh water.

So he lay there for two whole days, and then came two wild geese, or rather ganders, for they were two young men; they

136

had not been out of the egg very long, and that was why they were so cocky.

"Listen, young fellow," they said. "You're so ugly that we quite like you. Will you join us and be a bird of passage? Close by, in another marsh there are some lovely wild geese, all nice young girls, and they can all say 'Quack.' You're so ugly that you might appeal to them."

Two shots rang out—bang! bang!—both ganders fell dead among the reeds, and the water was reddened with their blood. Bang! bang! was heard again, and whole flocks of wild geese flew up from the reeds, and—bang! bang! bang! again and again. A great shoot was going on. The men were lying under cover all round the marsh, and some of them were even up in the trees whose branches stretched out above the reeds. Blue smoke drifted in among the dark trees and was carried far out over the water. Through the mud came the gun-dogs—splash! splash!—bending down the reeds and rushes on every side. The poor duckling was scared out of his wits, and tried to hide his head under his wing, when suddenly a fierce-looking dog came close to him, with his tongue hanging far out of his mouth, and his wild eyes gleaming horribly. He opened his jaws wide, showed his sharp teeth, and —splash! splash!—off he went without touching the duckling.

"Thank heaven!" he sighed. "I'm so ugly that even the dog won't bother to bite me!"

And so he lay perfectly still, while the shots rattled through the reeds as gun after gun was fired.

It was towards evening when everything quieted down, but the poor duckling dared not stir yet. He waited several hours before he looked about him, and then hurried away from the marsh as fast as he could. He ran over field and meadow, hardly able to fight against the strong wind.

Late that night he reached a wretched little hut, so wretched, in fact, that it did not know which way to fall, and that is why it remained standing upright. The wind whistled so fiercely round the duckling that the poor thing simply had to sit down on his little tail to resist it.

The storm grew worse and worse. Then he noticed that the door had come off one of its hinges and hung so crooked that he could slip into the room through the opening, and that is what he did.

An old woman lived here with her tom-cat and her hen. The cat, whom she called "Sonny," knew how to arch his back and purr; in fact he could even give out sparks, but for that you had to rub his fur the wrong way. The hen had little short legs and was called "Stumpy." She was an excellent layer and the old woman loved her as her own child.

Next morning they at once noticed the strange duckling; the cat began to purr and the hen to cluck.

"What's the matter?" asked the old woman, looking about her; but her eyes were not very good, and so she mistook the duckling for a fat duck that had lost her way. "What a windfall!" she said. "Now I shall have duck's eggs—if it doesn't happen to be a drake. We must make sure of that." So the duckling was taken on trial for three weeks, but not a single egg came along.

Now the cat was master of the house, and the hen was mistress, and they always said, "We, and the world;" for they imagined themselves to be not only half the world, but by far the better half. The duckling thought that other people might be allowed to have an opinion too, but the hen could not see that at all.

138

"Can you lay eggs?" she asked.

"No."

"Well, then, you'd better keep your mouth shut!"

And the cat said, "Can you arch your back, purr, and give out sparks?"

"No."

"Well, then, you can't have any opinion worth offering when sensible people are speaking."

The duckling sat in a corner, feeling very gloomy and depressed; then he suddenly thought of the fresh air and the bright sunshine, and such a longing came over him to swim in the water that he could not help telling the hen about it.

"What's the matter with you?" asked the hen. "You haven't got anything to do, that's why you get these silly ideas. Either lay eggs or purr and you'll soon be all right."

"But it's so delightful to swim in the water," said the duckling, "so delightful to get it over your head and dive down to the bottom!"

"Yes, it must be delightful!" said the hen. "You've gone crazy, I think. Ask the cat, the cleverest creature I know, if he likes swimming or diving. I say nothing of myself. Ask our mistress, the old woman, as well; no one in the world is wiser than she. Do you think she would like to swim, or to get the water over her head?"

"You don't understand me," said the duckling.

"Well, if we don't understand you, then who would? You surely don't imagine you're wiser than the cat or the old woman?—not to mention myself, of course. Don't give yourself such airs, child, but be grateful to your Maker for all the kindness you have received. Didn't you get into a warm room, and haven't you fallen in with people who can teach you a thing or two? But you talk such nonsense, it's no fun at all to have you about. Believe me, I wish you well. I tell you unpleasant things, but that's the way to know one's real friends. Come on, hurry up, see that you lay eggs, and do learn how to purr or to give out sparks!"

"I think I had better go out into the wide world," said the duckling.

"Please yourself," said the hen.

So the duckling went away: he swam in the water and dived down into it, but he was still snubbed by every creature because of his ugliness.

Autumn set in. The leaves in the woods turned yellow and brown: the wind caught them and whirled them about; up in the air it looked very cold. The clouds hung low, heavy with hail and snowflakes, and on the fence perched the raven, trembling with the cold and croaking, "Caw! Caw!" The mere thought of it was enough to make anybody shiver. The poor duckling was certainly to be pitied!

One evening, when the sun was setting in all its splendor, a large flock of big handsome birds came out of the bushes. The duckling had never before seen anything quite so beautiful as these birds. They were dazzlingly white, with long supple necks—they were swans! They uttered a most uncanny cry, and spread their splendid great wings to fly away from the cold regions, away to warmer countries, to open lakes. They rose so high, so very high in the air, that a strange feeling came over the ugly little duckling as he watched them. He turned round and round in the water like a wheel, craned his neck to follow their flight, and uttered a cry so loud and strange that it frightened him.

He could not forget those noble birds, those happy birds, and when they were lost to sight he dived down to the bottom

140

of the water; then when he came up again he was quite beside himself. He did not know what the birds were called, nor where they were flying to, and yet he loved them more than he had ever loved anything. He did not envy them in the least; it would never have occurred to him to want such beauty for himself. He would have been quite content if only the ducks would have put up with him—the poor ugly creature!

And the winter grew so cold, so bitterly cold. The duckling was forced to swim about in the water to keep it from freezing altogether, but every night the opening became smaller and smaller; at last it froze so hard that the ice made cracking noises, and the duckling had to keep on paddling to prevent the opening from closing up. In the end he was exhausted and lay quite still, caught in the ice.

Early next morning a farmer came by, and when he saw him he went on to the ice, broke it with his wooden shoe, and carried him home to his wife. There the duckling revived.

The children wanted to play with him, but he thought they meant to do him harm, so he fluttered, terrified, into the milk pail, splashing the milk all over the room. The woman screamed and threw up her hands in fright. Then he flew into the butter-tub, and from that into the flour-barrel and out again. What a sight he was! The woman shrieked and struck at him with the tongs. Laughing and shouting, the children fell over each other trying to catch him. Fortunately the door was open, so the duckling dashed out into the bushes and lay there in the newly fallen snow, as if in a daze.

It would be too sad, however, to tell all the trouble and misery he had to suffer during that cruel winter. When the sun began to shine warmly he found himself once more in the marsh among the reeds. The larks were singing—it was spring, beautiful spring!

Then suddenly he spread his wings; the sound of their

whirring made him realize how much stronger they had grown, and they carried him powerfully along. Before he knew it, he found himself in a great garden where the apple trees stood in bloom, and the lilac filled the air with its fragrance, bending down the long green branches over the meandering streams.

It was so lovely here, so full of the freshness of spring. And look! from out of the thicket in front of him came three beautiful white swans. They ruffled their feathers proudly, and floated so lightly on the water. The duckling recognized the glorious creatures, and felt a strange sadness come over him.

"I will fly near those royal birds, and they will peck me to death for daring to bring my ugly self near them. But that doesn't matter in the least! Better to be killed by them than to be bitten by the ducks, pecked by the hens, kicked by the girl in charge of the hen-run, and suffer untold agony in winter."

Then he flew into the water and swam towards the beautiful swans. They saw him and dashed at him with outspread rustling feathers. "Kill me," said the poor creature, and he bowed his head down upon the surface of the stream, expecting death. But what was this he saw mirrored in the clear water? He saw beneath him his own image, but it was no longer the image of an awkward dirty gray bird, ugly and repulsive —he himself was a swan!

It does not matter being born in a duckyard, if only one has lain in a swan's egg.

He felt quite glad to have been through so much trouble and adversity, for now he could fully appreciate not only his own good fortune, but also all the beauty that greeted him. The great swans swam round him and stroked him with their beaks.

Some little children came into the garden to throw bread

142

and corn into the water, and the youngest exclaimed, "There's a new one!" And the other children chimed in, "Yes, there's a new one!" They clapped their hands, danced about, and ran to fetch their father and mother.

Bread and cake were thrown into the water, and everyone said, "The new one is the most beautiful of all! He's so young and handsome!" And the old swans bowed to him.

That made him feel quite embarrassed, and he put his head under his wing, not knowing what it was all about. An overwhelming happiness filled him, and yet he was not at all proud, for a good heart never becomes proud.

He remembered how once he had been despised and persecuted; and now he heard everyone saying that he was the most beautiful of all beautiful birds.

And the lilac bushes dipped their branches into the water before him; and the sun shone warm and mild. He rustled his feathers and held his graceful neck high, and from the depths of his heart he joyfully exclaimed, "I never dreamt that so much happiness was possible when I was the ugly duckling."

THE Mole had been working very hard all the morning, spring-cleaning his little home. First with brooms, then with dusters; then on ladders and steps and chairs, with a brush and a pail of whitewash; till he had dust in his throat and eyes, and splashes of whitewash all over his black fur, and an aching back and weary arms. Spring was moving in the air above and in the earth below and around him, penetrating even his dark and lowly little house with its spirit of divine discontent and longing. It was small wonder, then, that he suddenly flung down his brush on the floor, said "Bother!" and "O blow!" and also "Hang spring-cleaning!" and bolted out of the house without even waiting to put on his coat. Something up above was calling him imperiously, and he made for the steep little tunnel which answered in his case to the gravelled carriage-drive owned by animals whose residences are nearer to the sun and air. So he scraped and scratched and scrabbled and scrooged, and then he scrooged again and scrabbled and scratched and scraped, working busily with his little paws and muttering to himself, "Up we go! Up we go!" till at last, pop! his snout came out into the sunlight, and he found himself rolling in the warm grass of a great meadow.

The River Bank

BY KENNETH GRAHAME

Illustrated by

Ernest H. Shepard

"This is fine!" he said to himself. "This is better than whitewashing!" The sunshine struck hot on his fur, soft breezes caressed his heated brow, and after the seclusion of the cellarage he had lived in so long the carol of happy birds fell on

144

his dulled hearing almost like a shout. Jumping off all his four legs at once, in the joy of living and the delight of spring without its cleaning, he pursued his way across the meadow till he reached the hedge on the further side.

"Hold up!" said an elderly rabbit at the gap. "Sixpence for the privilege of passing by the private road!" He was bowled over in an instant by the impatient and contemptuous Mole, who trotted along the side of the hedge chaffing the other rabbits as they peeped hurriedly from their holes to see what the row was about. "Onion-sauce! Onion-sauce!" he remarked jeeringly, and was gone before they could think of a thoroughly satisfactory reply. Then they all started grumbling at each other. "How *stupid* you are! Why didn't you tell him——" "Well, why didn't *you* say——" "You might have reminded him——" and so on, in the usual way; but, of course, it was then much too late, as is always the case.

It all seemed too good to be true. Hither and thither through the meadows he rambled busily, along the hedge-rows, across the copses, finding everywhere birds building, flowers budding, leaves thrusting—everything happy, and progressive, and occupied. And instead of having an uneasy conscience pricking him and whispering "Whitewash!" he somehow could only feel how jolly it was to

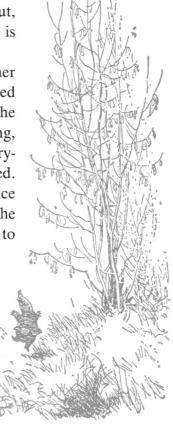

be the only idle dog among all these busy citizens. After all, the best part of a holiday is perhaps not so much to be resting yourself, as to see all the other fellows busy working.

He thought his happiness was complete when, as he meandered aimlessly along, suddenly he stood by the edge of a full-fed river. Never in his life had he seen a river before—this sleek, sinuous, full-bodied animal, chasing and chuckling, gripping things with a gurgle and leaving them with a laugh, to fling itself on fresh playmates that shook themselves free, and were caught and held again. All was a-shake and a-shiver—glints and gleams and sparkles, rustle and swirl, chatter and bubble. The Mole was bewitched, entranced, fascinated. By the side of the river he trotted as one trots, when very small, by the side of a man who holds one spellbound by exciting stories; and when tired at last, he sat on the bank, while the river still chattered on to him, a babbling

146

procession of the best stories in the world, sent from the heart of the earth to be told at last to the insatiable sea.

As he sat on the grass and looked across the river, a dark hole in the bank opposite, just above the water's edge, caught his eye, and dreamily he fell to considering what a nice snug dwelling place it would make for an animal with few wants and fond of a bijou riverside residence, above flood level and remote from noise and dust. As he gazed, something bright and small seemed to twinkle down in the heart of it, vanished, then twinkled once more like a tiny star. But it could hardly be a star in such an unlikely situation; and it was too glittering and small for a glow-worm. Then, as he looked, it winked at him, and so declared itself to be an eye; and a small face began gradually to grow up round it, like a frame round a picture.

A brown little face, with whiskers.

147

A grave round face, with the same twinkle in its eye that had first attracted his notice.

Small neat ears and thick silky hair.

It was the Water Rat!

Then the two animals stood and regarded each other cautiously.

"Hullo, Mole!" said the Water Rat.

"Hullo, Rat!" said the Mole.

"Would you like to come over?" inquired the Rat presently.

"Oh, it's all very well to *talk*," said the Mole, rather pettishly, he being new to a river and riverside life and its ways.

The Rat said nothing, but stooped and unfastened a rope and hauled on it; then lightly stepped into a little boat which the Mole had not observed. It was painted blue outside and white within, and was just the size for two animals; and the Mole's whole heart went out to it at once, even though he did not yet fully understand its uses.

The Rat sculled smartly across and made fast. Then he held up his fore-paw as the Mole stepped gingerly down. "Lean on that!" he said. "Now then, step lively!" and the Mole to his surprise and rapture found himself actually seated in the stern of a real boat.

"This has been a wonderful day!" said he, as the Rat shoved off and took to the sculls again. "Do you know, I've never been in a boat before in all my life."

"What?" cried the Rat, open-mouthed: "Never been in a—you never—well, I—what have you been doing, then?"

"Is it so nice as all that?" asked the Mole shyly, though he was quite prepared to believe it as he leant back in his seat and surveyed the cushions, the oars, the rowlocks, and all the fascinating fittings, and felt the boat sway lightly under him.

148

"Nice? It's the *only* thing," said the Water Rat solemnly, as he leaned forward for his stroke. "Believe me, my young friend, there is *nothing*—absolutely nothing—half so much worth doing as simply messing about in boats. Simply messing," he went on dreamily: "messing—about—in—boats; messing——"

"Look ahead, Rat!" cried the Mole suddenly.

It was too late. The boat struck the bank full tilt. The dreamer, the joyous oarsman, lay on his back at the bottom of the boat, his heels in the air.

"—about in boats—or *with* boats," the Rat went on composedly, picking himself up with a pleasant laugh. "In or out of 'em, it doesn't matter. Nothing seems really to matter, that's the charm of it. Whether you get away, or whether you don't; whether you arrive at your destination or whether you reach somewhere else, or whether you never get anywhere at all, you're always busy, and you never do anything in particular; and when you've done it there's always something else to do, and you can do it if you like, but you'd much better not. Look here! If you've really nothing else on hand this morning, supposing we drop down the river together, and have a long day of it?"

The Mole waggled his toes from sheer happiness, spread his chest with a sigh of full contentment, and leaned back blissfully into the soft cushions. *"What* a day I'm having!" he said. "Let us start at once!"

"Hold hard a minute, then!" said the Rat. He looped the painter through a ring in his landing-stage, climbed up into his hole above, and after a short interval reappeared staggering under a fat, wicker luncheon-basket.

"Shove that under your feet," he observed to the Mole, as

he passed it down into the boat. Then he untied the painter and took the sculls again.

"What's inside it?" asked the Mole, wriggling with curiosity.

"There's cold chicken inside it," replied the Rat briefly; "coldtonguecoldhamcoldbeefpickledgherkinssaladfrenchrolls-cresssandwidgespottedmeatgingerbeerlemonadesodawater—"

"O stop, stop," cried the Mole in ecstasies: "This is too much!"

"Do you really think so?" inquired the Rat seriously. "It's only what I always take on these little excursions; and the other animals are always telling me that I'm a mean beast and cut it *very* fine!"

The Mole never heard a word he was saying. Absorbed in the new life he was entering upon, intoxicated with the sparkle, the ripple, the scents and the sounds and the sunlight, he trailed a paw in the water and dreamed long wak-

150

ing dreams. The Water Rat, like the good little fellow he was, sculled steadily on and forebore to disturb him.

"I like your clothes awfully, old chap," he remarked after some half an hour or so had passed. "I'm going to get a black velvet smoking suit myself some day, as soon as I can afford it."

"I beg your pardon," said the Mole, pulling himself together with an effort. "You must think me very rude; but all this is so new to me. So—this—is—a—River!"

"*The* River," corrected the Rat.

"And you really live by the river? What a jolly life!"

"By it and with it and on it and in it," said the Rat. "It's brother and sister to me, and aunts, and company, and food and drink, and (naturally) washing. It's my world, and I don't want any other. What it hasn't got is not worth having, and what it doesn't know is not worth knowing. Lord! the times we've had together! Whether in winter or summer, spring or autumn, it's always got its fun and its excitements. When the floods are on in February, and my cellars and basement are brimming with drink that's no good to me, and the brown water runs by my best bedroom window; or again when it all drops away and shows patches of mud that smells like plum-cake, and the rushes and weed clog the channels, and I can potter about dry-shod over most of the bed of it and find fresh food to eat, and things careless people have dropped out of boats!"

"But isn't it a bit dull at times?" the Mole ventured to ask. "Just you and the river, and no one else to pass a word with?"

"No one else to—well, I mustn't be hard on you," said the Rat with forbearance. "You're new to it, and of course you don't know. The bank is so crowded nowadays that many people are moving away altogether. O no, it isn't what it used to be, at all. Otters, kingfishers, dabchicks, moorhens, all of them about all day long and always wanting you to *do* something—as if a fellow had no business of his own to attend to!"

"What lies over *there?*" asked the Mole, waving a paw towards a background of woodland that darkly framed the water-meadows on one side of the river.

"That? O, that's just the Wild Wood," said the Rat shortly. "We don't go there very much, we river-bankers."

"Aren't they—aren't they very *nice* people in there?" said the Mole a trifle nervously.

"W-e-ll," replied the Rat, "let me see. The squirrels are all right. *And* the rabbits—some of 'em, but rabbits are a mixed lot. And then there's Badger, of course. He lives right in the heart of it; wouldn't live anywhere else, either, if you paid him to do it. Dear old Badger! Nobody interferes with *him*. They'd better not," he added significantly.

"Why, who *should* interfere with him?" asked the Mole.

"Well, of course—there—are others," exclaimed the Rat in a hesitating sort of way. "Weasels—and stoats—and foxes—and so on. They're all right in a way—I'm very good friends with them—pass the time of day when we meet, and all that —but they break out sometimes, there's no denying it, and

152

then—well, you can't really trust them, and that's the fact."

The Mole knew well that it is quite against animal-etiquette to dwell on possible trouble ahead, or even to allude to it; so he dropped the subject.

"And beyond the Wild Wood again?" he asked: "Where it's all blue and dim, and one sees what may be hills or perhaps they mayn't, and something like the smoke of towns, or is it only cloud-drift?"

"Beyond the Wild Wood comes the Wide World," said the Rat. "And that's something that doesn't matter, either to you or me. I've never been there, and I'm never going, nor you either, if you've got any sense at all. Don't ever refer to it again, please. Now then! Herc's our backwater at last, where we're going to lunch."

Leaving the main stream, they now passed into what seemed at first sight like a little land-locked lake. Green turf sloped down to either edge, brown snaky tree-roots gleamed below the surface of the quiet water, while ahead of them the silvery shoulder and foamy tumble of a weir, arm-in-arm with a restless dripping mill-wheel, that held up in its turn a grey-gabled mill-house, filled the air with a soothing murmur of sound, dull and smothery, yet with little clear voices speaking up cheerfully out of it at intervals. It was so very beautiful that the Mole could only hold up both fore-paws and gasp, "O my! O my! O my!"

The Rat brought the boat alongside the bank, made her fast, helped the still awkward Mole safely ashore, and swung out the luncheon-basket. The Mole begged as a favour to be allowed to unpack it all by himself; and the Rat was very pleased to indulge him, and to sprawl at full length on the grass and rest, while his excited friend shook out the table-cloth and spread it, took out all the mysterious packets one

153

by one and arranged their contents in due order, still gasping,
"O my! O my!" at each fresh revelation. When all was ready,
the Rat said, "Now, pitch in, old fellow!" and the Mole was
indeed very glad to obey, for he had started his spring-cleaning at a very early hour that morning, as people *will* do, and
had not paused for bite or sup; and he had been through a
very great deal since that distant time which now seemed so
many days ago.

"What are you looking at?" said the Rat presently, when
the edge of their hunger was somewhat dulled, and the
Mole's eyes were able to wander off the tablecloth a little.

"I am looking," said the Mole, "at a streak of bubbles
that I see travelling along the surface of the water. That is a
thing that strikes me as funny."

"Bubbles? Oho!" said the Rat, and chirruped cheerily in
an inviting sort of way.

A broad glistening muzzle showed itself above the edge
of the bank, and the Otter hauled himself out and shook the
water from his coat.

"Greedy beggars!" he observed, making for the provender.
"Why didn't you invite me, Ratty?"

"This was an impromptu affair," explained the Rat. "By
the way—my friend Mr. Mole."

"Proud, I'm sure," said the Otter, and the two animals
were friends forthwith.

"Such a rumpus everywhere!" continued the Otter. "All the

154

world seems out on the river to-day. I came up this backwater to try and get a moment's peace, and then stumble upon you fellows!—At least—I beg pardon—I don't exactly mean that, you know."

There was a rustle behind him, proceeding from a hedge wherein last year's leaves still clung thick, and a stripy head, with high shoulders behind it, peered forth on them.

"Come on, old Badger!" shouted the Rat.

The Badger trotted forward a pace or two; then grunted, "H'm! Company," and turned his back and disappeared from view.

"That's *just* the sort of fellow he is!" observed the disappointed Rat. "Simply hates Society! Now we shan't see any more of him to-day. Well, tell us *who's* out on the river?"

"Toad's out, for one," replied the Otter. "In his brand-new wager-boat; new togs, new everything!"

The two animals looked at each other and laughed.

"Once, it was nothing but sailing," said the Rat. "Then he tired of that and took to punting. Nothing would please him but to punt all day and every day, and a nice mess he made of it. Last year it was house-boating, and we all had to go and stay with him in his house-boat, and pretend we liked it. He was going to spend the rest of his life in a house-boat. It's all the same, whatever he takes up; he gets tired of it, and starts on something fresh."

"Such a good fellow, too," remarked the Otter reflectively: "But no stability—especially in a boat!"

From where they sat they could get a glimpse of the main stream across the island that separated them; and just then a wager-boat flashed into view, the rower—a short, stout figure —splashing badly and rolling a good deal, but working his hardest. The Rat stood up and hailed him, but Toad—for it was he—shook his head and settled sternly to his work.

"He'll be out of the boat in a minute if he rolls like that," said the Rat, sitting down again.

"Of course he will," chuckled the Otter. "Did I ever tell you that good story about Toad and the lock-keeper? It happened this way. Toad . . ."

An errant May-fly swerved unsteadily athwart the current in the intoxicated fashion affected by young bloods of May-flies seeing life. A swirl of water and a "cloop!" and the May-fly was visible no more.

Neither was the Otter.

The Mole looked down. The voice was still in his ears, but the turf whereon he had sprawled was clearly vacant. Not an Otter to be seen, as far as the distant horizon.

But again there was a streak of bubbles on the surface of the river.

The Rat hummed a tune, and the Mole recollected that

156

animal-etiquette forbade any sort of comment on the sudden disappearance of one's friends at any moment, for any reason or no reason whatever.

"Well, well," said the Rat, "I suppose we ought to be moving. I wonder which of us had better pack the luncheon-basket?" He did not speak as if he was frightfully eager for the treat.

"O, please let me," said the Mole. So, of course, the Rat let him.

Packing the basket was not quite such pleasant work as unpacking the basket. It never is. But the Mole was bent on enjoying everything, and although just when he had got the basket packed and strapped up tightly he saw a plate staring up at him from the grass, and when the job had been done again the Rat pointed out a fork which anybody ought to have seen, and last of all, behold! the mustard pot, which he had been sitting on without knowing it—still, somehow, the thing got finished at last, without much loss of temper.

The afternoon sun was getting low as the Rat sculled gently homewards in a dreamy mood, murmuring poetry-things over to himself, and not paying much attention to Mole. But the Mole was very full of lunch, and self-satis-faction, and pride, and already quite at home in a boat (so he thought) and was getting a bit restless besides: and presently he said, "Ratty! Please, *I* want to row, now!"

The Rat shook his head with a smile. "Not yet, my young friend," he said—"wait till you've had a few lessons. It's not so easy as it looks."

The Mole was quiet for a minute or two. But he began to feel more and more jealous of Rat, sculling so strongly and so easily along, and his pride began to whisper that he could do it every bit as well. He jumped up and seized the sculls so

157

suddenly, that the Rat, who was gazing out over the water and saying more poetry-things to himself, was taken by surprise and fell backwards off his seat with his legs in the air for the second time, while the triumphant Mole took his place and grabbed the sculls with entire confidence.

"Stop it, you *silly* ass!" cried the Rat, from the bottom of the boat. "You can't do it! You'll have us over!"

The Mole flung his sculls back with a flourish, and made a great dig at the water. He missed the surface altogether, his legs flew up above his head, and he found himself lying on the top of the prostrate Rat. Greatly alarmed, he made a grab at the side of the boat, and the next moment—Sploosh!

Over went the boat, and he found himself struggling in the water.

O my, how cold the water was, and O, how very wet it felt. How it sang in his ears as he went down, down, down! How bright and welcome the sun looked as he rose to the surface coughing and spluttering! How black was his despair when he felt himself sinking again! Then a firm paw gripped him by the back of his neck. It was the Rat, and he was evidently laughing—the Mole could *feel* him laughing, right down his arm and through his paw, and so into his— the Mole's—neck.

The Rat got hold of a scull and shoved it under the Mole's arm; then he did the same by the other side of him and, swimming behind, propelled the helpless animal to shore, hauled him out, and set him down on the bank, a squashy, pulpy lump of misery.

When the Rat had rubbed him down a bit, and wrung some of the wet out of him, he said, "Now, then, old fellow! Trot up and down the towing-path as hard as you can, till you're warm and dry again, while I dive for the luncheon-basket."

So the dismal Mole, wet without and ashamed within, trotted about till he was fairly dry, while the Rat plunged into the water again, recovered the boat, righted her and made her fast, fetched his floating property to shore by degrees, and finally dived successfully for the luncheon-basket and struggled to land with it.

When all was ready for a start once more, the Mole, limp and dejected, took his seat in the stern of the boat; and as they set off, he said in a low voice, broken with emotion, "Ratty, my generous friend! I am very sorry indeed for my foolish and ungrateful conduct. My heart quite fails me when I think how I might have lost that beautiful luncheon-basket. Indeed, I have been a complete ass, and I know it. Will you overlook it this once and forgive me, and let things go on as before?"

"That's all right, bless you!" responded the Rat cheerily. "What's a little wet to a Water Rat? I'm more in the water than out of it most days. Don't you think any more about it; and, look here! I really think you had better come and stop with me for a little time. It's very plain and rough, you know —not like Toad's house at all—but you haven't seen that yet; still, I can make you comfortable. And I'll teach you to row,

159

and to swim, and you'll soon be as handy on the water as any of us."

The Mole was so touched by his kind manner of speaking that he could find no voice to answer him; and he had to brush away a tear or two with the back of his paw. But the Rat kindly looked in another direction, and presently the Mole's spirits revived again, and he was even able to give some straight back-talk to a couple of moorhens who were sniggering to each other about his bedraggled appearance.

When they got home, the Rat made a bright fire in the parlour, and planted the Mole in an arm-chair in front of it, having fetched down a dressing-gown and slippers for him, and told him river stories till supper-time. Very thrilling stories they were, too, to an earth-dwelling animal like Mole. Stories about weirs, and sudden floods, and leaping pike, and steamers that flung hard bottles—at least bottles were certainly flung, and from steamers so presumably by them; and about herons, and how particular they were whom they spoke to; and about adventures down drains, and night-fishings with Otter, or excursions far afield with Badger. Supper was a most cheerful meal; but very shortly afterwards a terribly sleepy Mole had to be escorted upstairs by his considerate host, to the best bedroom, where he soon laid his head on his pillow in great peace and contentment, knowing that his new-found friend the River was lapping the sill of his window.

This day was only the first of many similar ones for the emancipated Mole, each of them longer and fuller of interest as the ripening summer moved onward. He learnt to swim and to row, and entered into the joy of running water; and with his ear to the reed-stems he caught, at intervals, something of what the wind went whispering so constantly among them.

160

ONE Friday night in November Homer overheard his mother talking on the telephone to Aunt Agnes over in Centerburg. "I'll stop by with the car in about half an hour and we can go to the meeting together," she said, because tonight was the night the Ladies' Club was meeting to discuss plans for a box social and to knit and sew for the Red Cross.

"I think I'll come along and keep Uncle Ulysses company while you and Aunt Agnes are at the meeting," said Homer.

So after Homer had combed his hair and his mother had looked to see if she had her knitting instructions and the right size needles, they started for town.

Homer's Uncle Ulysses and Aunt Agnes have a very up-and-coming lunch room over in Centerburg, just across from the court house on the town square. Uncle Ulysses is a man with advanced

The Doughnuts

BY ROBERT McCLOSKEY

Illustrated by Robert McCloskey

ideas and a weakness for labor saving devices. He equipped the lunch room with automatic toasters, automatic coffee maker, automatic dish washer, and an automatic doughnut maker. All the latest things in labor saving devices. Aunt Agnes would throw up her hands and sigh every time Uncle Ulysses bought a new labor saving device. Sometimes she became unkindly disposed toward him for days and days. She was of the opinion that Uncle Ulysses just frittered away his spare time over at the barber shop with the sheriff and the boys, so, what was the good of a labor-saving device that gave you more time to fritter?

161

When Homer and his mother got to Centerburg they stopped at the lunch room, and after Aunt Agnes had come out and said, "My, how that boy does grow!" which was what she always said, she went off with Homer's mother in the car, Homer went into the lunch room and said, "Howdy, Uncle Ulysses!"

"Oh, hello, Homer. You're just in time," said Uncle Ulysses. "I've been going over this automatic doughnut machine, oiling the machinery and cleaning the works . . . wonderful things, these labor-saving devices."

"Yep," agreed Homer, and he picked up a cloth and started polishing the metal trimmings while Uncle Ulysses tinkered with the inside workings.

"Opfwo-oof! !" sighed Uncle Ulysses and, "Look here, Homer, you've got a mechanical mind. See if you can find where these two pieces fit in. I'm going across to the barber shop for a spell, 'cause there's somethin' I've got to talk to the sheriff about. There won't be much business here until the double feature is over and I'll be back before then."

Then as Uncle Ulysses went out the door he said, "Uh, Homer, after you get the pieces in place, would you mind mixing up a batch of doughnut batter and put it in the machine? You could turn the switch and make a few doughnuts to have on hand for the crowd after the movie . . . if you don't mind."

"O.K.," said Homer, "I'll take care of everything."

A few minutes later a customer came in and said, "Good evening, Bud."

Homer looked up from putting the last piece in the doughnut machine and said, "Good evening, Sir, what can I do for you?"

162

"Well, young feller, I'd like a cup o' coffee and some doughnuts," said the customer.

"I'm sorry, Mister, but we won't have any doughnuts for about half an hour, until I can mix some dough and start this machine. I could give you some very fine sugar rolls instead."

"Well, Bud, I'm in no real hurry so I'll just have a cup o' coffee and wait around a bit for the doughnuts. Fresh doughnuts are always worth waiting for is what I always say."

"O.K.," said Homer, and he drew a cup of coffee from Uncle Ulysses' super automatic coffee maker.

"Nice place you've got here," said the customer.

"Oh, yes," replied Homer, "this is a very up and coming lunch room with all the latest improvements."

"Yes," said the stranger, "must be a good business. I'm in business too. A traveling man in outdoor advertising. I'm a sandwich man, Mr. Gabby's my name."

"My name is Homer. I'm glad to meet you, Mr. Gabby. It must be a fine profession, traveling and advertising sandwiches."

"Oh, no," said Mr. Gabby, "I don't advertise sandwiches, I just wear any kind of an ad, one sign on front and one sign on behind, this way . . . Like a sandwich. Ya know what I mean?"

"Oh, I see. That must be fun, and you travel too?" asked Homer as he got out the flour and the baking powder.

"Yeah, I ride the rods between jobs, on freight trains, ya know what I mean?"

"Yes, but isn't that dangerous?" asked Homer.

"Of course there's a certain amount a risk, but you take any method a travel these days, it's all dangerous. Ya know what I mean? Now take airplanes for instance . . ."

163

Just then a large shiny black car stopped in front of the lunch room and a chauffeur helped a lady out of the rear door. They both came inside and the lady smiled at Homer and said, "We've stopped for a light snack. Some doughnuts and coffee would be simply marvelous."

Then Homer said, "I'm sorry, Ma'm, but the doughnuts won't be ready until I make this batter and start Uncle Ulysses' doughnut machine."

"Well now aren't *you* the clever young man to know how to make *doughnuts!*"

"Well," blushed Homer, "I've really never done it before but I've got a receipt to follow."

"Now, young man, you simply must allow me to help. You know, I haven't made doughnuts for years, but I know the best receipt for doughnuts. It's marvelous, and we really must use it."

"But, Ma'm . . ." said Homer.

"Now just *wait* till you see and taste these doughnuts," said the lady. "Do you have an apron?" she asked, as she took off her fur coat and her rings and her jewelry and rolled up her sleeves. "Charles," she said to the chauffeur, "hand me that baking powder, that's right, and, young man, we'll need some nutmeg."

So Homer and the chauffeur stood by and handed things and cracked the eggs while the lady mixed and stirred. Mr. Gabby sat on his stool, sipped his coffee, and looked on with great interest.

"There!" said the lady when all of the ingredients were mixed. "Just *wait* till you taste these doughnuts!"

"It looks like an awful lot of batter," said Homer as he stood on a chair and poured it into the doughnut machine with the help of the chauffeur. "It's about *ten* times as much as

164

Uncle Ulysses ever makes."

"But wait till you taste them!" said the lady with an eager look and a smile.

Homer got down from the chair and pushed a button on the machine marked, "Start." Rings of batter started dropping into the hot fat. After a ring of batter was cooked on one side an automatic gadget turned it over and the other side would cook. Then another automatic gadget gave the doughnut a little push and it rolled neatly down a little chute, all ready to eat.

"That's a simply *fascinating* machine," said the lady as she waited for the first doughnut to roll out.

"Here, young man, *you* must have the first one. Now isn't that just *too* delicious? Isn't it simply marvelous?"

"Yes, Ma'm, it's very good," replied Homer as the lady handed doughnuts to Charles and to Mr. Gabby and asked if they didn't think they were simply divine doughnuts.

"It's an old family receipt!" said the lady with pride.

Homer poured some coffee for the lady and her chauffeur and for Mr. Gabby, and a glass of milk for himself. Then they all sat down at the lunch counter to enjoy another few doughnuts apiece.

"I'm so glad you enjoy my doughnuts," said the lady. "But now, Charles, we really must be going. If you will just take this apron, Homer, and put two dozen doughnuts in a bag to take along, we'll be on our way. And, Charles, don't forget to pay the young man." She rolled down her sleeves and put on

165

her jewelry, then Charles managed to get her into her big fur coat.

"Good night, young man, I haven't had so much fun in years. I *really* haven't!" said the lady, as she went out the door and into the big shiny car.

"Those are sure good doughnuts," said Mr. Gabby as the car moved off.

"You bet!" said Homer. Then he and Mr. Gabby stood and watched the automatic doughnut machine make doughnuts.

After a few dozen more doughnuts had rolled down the little chute, Homer said, "I guess that's about enough doughnuts to sell to the after theater customers. I'd better turn the machine off for a while."

Homer pushed the button marked "Stop" and there was a little click, but nothing happened. The rings of batter kept right on dropping into the hot fat, and an automatic gadget kept right on turning them over, and another automatic gadget kept right on giving them a little push and the doughnuts kept right on rolling down the little chute, all ready to eat.

"That's funny," said Homer, "I'm sure that's the right button!" He pushed it again but the automatic doughnut maker kept right on making doughnuts.

"Well I guess I must have put one of those pieces in backwards," said Homer.

"Then it might stop if you pushed the button marked "Start," said Mr. Gabby.

Homer did, and the doughnuts still kept rolling down the little chute, just as regular as a clock can tick.

"I guess we could sell a few more doughnuts," said Homer, "but I'd better telephone Uncle Ulysses over at the

166

barber shop." Homer gave the number and while he waited for someone to answer he counted thirty-seven doughnuts roll down the chute.

Finally someone answered "Hello! This is the sarber bhop, I mean the barber shop."

"Oh, hello, sheriff. This is Homer. Could I speak to Uncle Ulysses?"

"Well, he's playing pinochle right now," said the sheriff. "Anythin' I can tell 'im?"

"Yes," said Homer. "I pushed the button marked *stop* on the doughnut machine but the rings of batter keep right on dropping into the hot fat, and an automatic gadget keeps right on turning them over, and another automatic gadget keeps giving them a little push, and the doughnuts keep right on rolling down the little chute! It won't stop!"

"O.K. Wold the hire, I mean, hold the wire and I'll tell 'im!" Then Homer looked over his shoulder and counted another twenty-one doughnuts roll down the little chute, all ready to eat. Then the sheriff said, "He'll be right over. . . . Just gotta finish this hand."

"That's good," said Homer. "G'by, sheriff."

The window was full of doughnuts by now so Homer and Mr. Gabby had to hustle around and start stacking them on plates and trays and lining them up on the counter.

"Sure are a lot of doughnuts!" said Homer.

"You bet!" said Mr. Gabby. "I lost count at twelve hundred and two and that was quite a while back."

People had begun to gather outside the lunch room window, and someone was saying, "There are almost as many doughnuts as there are people in Centerburg, and I wonder how in tarnation Ulysses thinks he can sell all of 'em!"

Every once in a while somebody would come inside and buy some, but while somebody bought two to eat and a dozen to take home, the machine made three dozen more.

By the time Uncle Ulysses and the sheriff arrived and pushed through the crowd, the lunch room was a calamity of doughnuts! Doughnuts in the window, doughnuts piled high on the shelves, doughnuts stacked on plates, doughnuts lined up twelve deep all along the counter, and doughnuts still rolling down the little chute, just as regular as a clock can tick.

"Hello, Sheriff, hello, Uncle Ulysses, we're having a little trouble here," said Homer.

"Well, I'll be dunked! !" said Uncle Ulysses.

"Derned ef you won't be when Aggy gits home," said the sheriff.

"Mighty fine doughnuts though. What'll you do with 'em all, Ulysses?"

Uncle Ulysses groaned and said,. "What will Aggy say? We'll never sell 'em all."

Then Mr. Gabby, who hadn't said anything for a long time, stopped piling doughnuts and said, "What you need is an advertising man. Ya know what I mean? You got the doughnuts, ya gotta create a market . . . Understand? It's balancing the demand with the supply . . . That sort of thing."

"Yep!" said Homer. "Mr. Gabby's right. We have to enlarge our market. He's an advertising sandwich man, so if we hire him, he can walk up and down in front of the theater and get the customers."

"You're hired, Mr. Gabby!" said Uncle Ulysses.

Then everybody pitched in to paint the signs and to get

168

Mr. Gabby sandwiched between. They painted "SALE ON DOUGHNUTS" in big letters on the window too.

Meanwhile the rings of batter kept right on dropping into the hot fat, and an automatic gadget kept right on turning them over, and another automatic gadget kept right on giving them a little push, and the doughnuts kept right on rolling down the little chute, just as regular as a clock can tick.

"I certainly hope this advertising works," said Uncle Ulysses, wagging his head. "Aggy'll certainly throw a fit if it don't."

The sheriff went outside to keep order, because there was quite a crowd by now—all looking at the doughnuts and guessing how many thousand there were, and watching new ones roll down the little chute, just as regular as a clock can tick. Homer and Uncle Ulysses kept stacking doughnuts. Once in a while somebody bought a few, but not very often.

Then Mr. Gabby came back and said, "Say, you know there's not

much use o' me advertisin' at the theater. The show's all over, and besides almost everybody in town is out front watching that machine make doughnuts!"

"Zeus!" said Uncle Ulysses. "We must get rid of these doughnuts before Aggy gets here!"

"Looks like you will have ta hire a truck to waul 'em ahay, I mean haul them away! !" said the sheriff who had just come in. Just then there was a noise and a shoving out front and the lady from the shiny black car and her chauffeur came pushing through the crowd and into the lunch room.

"Oh, gracious!" she gasped, ignoring the doughnuts, "I've lost my diamond bracelet, and I know I left it here on the counter," she said, pointing to a place where the doughnuts were piled in stacks of two dozen.

"Yes, Ma'm, I guess you forgot it when you helped make the batter," said Homer.

Then they moved all the doughnuts around and looked for the diamond bracelet, but they couldn't find it anywhere. Meanwhile the doughnuts kept rolling down the little chute, just as regular as a clock can tick.

After they had looked all around the sheriff cast a suspicious eye on Mr. Gabby, but Homer said, "He's all right, sheriff, he didn't take it. He's a friend of mine."

Then the lady said, "I'll offer a reward of one hundred dollars for that bracelet! It really *must* be found! . . . it *really* must!"

"Now don't you worry, lady," said the sheriff, "I'll get your bracelet back!"

"Zeus! This is terrible!" said Uncle Ulysses. "First all of these doughnuts and then on top of all that, a lost diamond bracelet . . ."

Mr. Gabby tried to comfort him, and he said, "There's al-

170

ways a bright side. That machine'll probably run outta batter in an hour or two."

If Gabby hadn't been quick on his feet Uncle Ulysses would have knocked him down, sure as fate.

Then while the lady wrung her hands and said, "We must find it, we *must!*" and Ulysses was moaning about what Aunt Agnes would say, and the sheriff was eyeing Mr. Gabby, Homer sat down and thought hard.

Before twenty more doughnuts could roll down the little chute he shouted, "SAY! I know where the bracelet is! It was lying here on the counter and got mixed up in the batter by mistake! The bracelet is cooked inside one of these doughnuts!"

"Why . . . I really believe you're right," said the lady through her tears. "Isn't that *amazing?* Simply *amazing!*"

"I'll be durn'd!" said the sheriff.

"Ohh-h!" moaned Uncle Ulysses. "Now we have to break up all of these doughnuts to find it. Think of the *pieces!* Think of the *crumbs!* Think of what *Aggy* will say!"

"Nope," said Homer. "We won't have to break them up. I've got a plan."

So Homer and the advertising man took some cardboard and some paint and printed another sign. They put this sign in the window, and the sandwich man wore two more signs that said the same thing and walked around in the crowd out front.

THEN . . . The doughnuts began to sell! *Everybody* wanted to buy doughnuts, *dozens* of doughnuts!

And that's not all. Everybody bought coffee to dunk the

FRESH DOUGHNUTS 2 FOR 5¢
WHILE THEY LAST
$100.⁰⁰ PRIZE
FOR FINDING A BRACELET INSIDE A DOUGHNUT
P.S. YOU HAVE TO GIVE THE BRACELET BACK

doughnuts in too. Those that didn't buy coffee bought milk or soda. It kept Homer and the lady and the chauffeur and Uncle Ulysses and the sheriff busy waiting on the people who wanted to buy doughnuts.

When all but the last couple of hundred doughnuts had been sold, Rupert Black shouted, "I GAWT IT! !" and sure enough . . . there was the diamond bracelet inside of his doughnut!

Then Rupert went home with a hundred dollars, the citizens of Centerburg went home full of doughnuts, the lady and her chauffeur drove off with the diamond bracelet, and Homer went home with his mother when she stopped by with Aunt Aggy.

As Homer went out of the door he heard Mr. Gabby say, "Neatest trick of merchandising I ever seen," and Aunt Aggy was looking skeptical while Uncle Ulysses was saying, "The rings of batter kept right on dropping into the hot fat, and the automatic gadget kept right on turning them over, and the other automatic gadget kept right on giving them a little push, and the doughnuts kept right on rolling down the little chute just as regular as a clock can tick—they just kept right on a comin', an' a comin', an' a comin', an' a comin'."

THREE plump mandarins hid behind a single tiny rose bush. The chancellor crawled under a chair. All courtiers fell upon their chins, and shivering, prayed that soft words might prevail.

For no slight reason did they shiver and hide and pray. King Yang Lang was angry. And he was an old-fashioned monarch, living in the long ago. Nowadays, any greasy kitchen lout may tweak a King's beard, and go forth to boast of his bravery. But then-a-days, Kings were Kings, and their swords were ever sharp.

King Yang Lang was such a ruler—and more angry than is good to see. His face was purple, and his voice boomed like a battle drum. "Keeper of the Treasury, has all my gold been used to make weights for fishing lines?"

Time after time the treasurer knocked his head against the paving. "Most Glorious and Peaceful Monarch, your gold is so plentiful that seven years must pass before I can finish counting the larger bars—ten years more for the smaller."

Pies of the Princess

BY ARTHUR BOWIE CHRISMAN

Illustrated by Else Hasselriis

That was rather pleasant news. The King's voice lost some of its harshness. "What of ivory? Has all my ivory been burned for firewood, a pot to boil?"

The treasurer continued to knock his head. "Supreme Ruler of The World and The Stars, your ivory completely fills a hundred large and closely guarded vaults."

The King hadn't dreamed that his wealth was so vast. His voice was not more than moderately furious as he asked:

173

"For what reason have you disposed of my jade? Do you mean to say that my jade has been used to build a stable for donkeys?"

Tap, tap, tap, went the treasurer's head on marble paving: "Oh, Powerful Potentate, the store of green jade grows larger each day. Your precious white jade is worth more than green, and gold and ivory combined. It is all quite safe, under lock and key and watchful spears."

The King was astonished and put in somewhat better humor. His voice was no louder than thunder as he again questioned the treasurer. "Then why, tell me why is my daughter, the Princess Chin Uor, not given suitable toys. If the treasury holds gold and ivory and jade, why is my daughter compelled to use toys of common clay?"

The treasurer could not explain: "Monarch whose word compels the sun to rise, we have pleaded with the wee Princess Chin Uor. We have given her a thousand dolls of solid gold, with silver cradles for each, cradles set with rubies—and the dolls have eyes of lustrous black pearl. For the princess we have made ivory cats, and ivory mice for the cats to catch —two thousand of each. For the princess we have fashioned from jade, lovely tossing balls, wonderful dishes, and puppy dogs that bark and come when called. Yet, the princess ignores these things . . . and makes mud pies—MUD PIES. Mightiest Majesty, I do not know why, unless it may be that the princess is a girl, as well as a princess."

A trifle relieved, King Yang Lang passed into the garden. Beside the river bank he found his daughter, the Princess Chin Uor, or Princess Many Dimples—for that is the meaning

174

of Chin Uor. Nurses standing near kept watch upon wheelbarrows spilling over with golden dolls. But Chin Uor had no thought for such toys. Her royal hands shaped the tastiest of mud pies. Very pretty pies they were—made of white clay.

The King said: "Littlest and most beautiful daughter, the golden dolls are longing for your touch. Why do you not please them? It is not seemly for a princess to dabble in clay. Then why do you make pies?"

The princess had a very good answer ready. "Because, Daddy, I want to make pies. This nice large one is for your dinner."

The King was so shocked that he could say nothing more. Mud pies for a King's dinner? Such nonsense. His Majesty was scandalized at the thought. He departed in haste.

But the Princess Chin Uor smiled and kneaded more and more pies. And when she had made enough she placed them in a wheelbarrow and trundled them to the palace.

And now the story changes. Far away to the west, in a mountain named Huge Rocks Piled, the famous dragon, Oo Loong, made his home. This fierce dragon was a creature of consuming greed. He was ever hungry and anxious to dine. A rabbit or an elephant—nothing was too large, nothing too small. A turtle or a jellyfish—nothing was too hard, nothing too soft. A man he considered fine eating. Boys he liked somewhat better. Girls? Girls were far superior to boys—in the dragon's opinion.

Much sorrow this ferocious *loong* had created in His Majesty's kingdom. A reward of one hundred silver pieces had been offered for the dragon's horns, two hundred for his ears. Magicians had worked charms to slay him—only themselves to be slain. Hunters had loaded their jingals with yellow paper, and had fired where the dragon was thickest, fired

175

where he was thinnest—only to be eaten—their guns with them. Made angry by the loss of so many people, King Yang Lang marched an army into the Mountain of Huge Rocks Piled. And the army was well armed with thumping drums and fifes and smoking guns.

Then the dragon became doubly furious and ferocious. To punish King Yang Lang, he resolved to visit the palace. That, he knew, would cause the army to be withdrawn. Accordingly, at the hour of deepest slumber, darksome mid of night, he prowled round Yang Lang's palace, seeking entrance. He had no easy task. Upon the King's door were pictures, also the word "Chi," written in gold. And so that door was well protected. The Queen's door likewise was dragon proof. It was covered with whole sentences taken from the black book of Hu Po, master magician. The door that led to where Princess Chin Uor slept was made strong by magic words and symbols. More of Hu Po's sorcery. Useless to prowl there. Dangerous to prowl there. The dragon was a knowing beast and prudent. The signs were against him. Hence, he tarried not, but crawled down the hallway in leaving.

A wheelbarrow stood in his path. He could not pass to the right. To the left he could not pass. Nor could he leap over the obstruction. But the dragon was not one to be baffled by such a weak and wooden contrivance. His huge mouth opened and his white hot breath rushed forth. In a twinkling the wooden barrow vanished. Like a butter cake dropped upon the summer sun it melted, burned to a cinder of nothingness.

Now the wheelbarrow thus destroyed was the property of the little Princess Chin Uor. In it had been golden dolls, dolls of the princess. The dolls were dolls no longer. Under the

176

dragon's fiery breath they changed to a pool of liquid gold. The hard gold became soft and flowing.

In the barrow had been pretty mud pies, pies of the princess. Under the dragon's burning breath they were changed to discs of stony hardness. The soft clay took on a hardness as of flint. The princess had wished her pies to dry. And her wish had been granted.

Next morning, the palace, from presence room to pantry, buzzed with excitment. Oo Loong had dared intrude within the royal dwelling. It could not be doubted. He had left his footprints in the molten gold, and the gold, in hardening, had preserved his tracks.

Witches and wizards came to make more able charms. Messengers galloped away to summon the distant army. The King raged and roared. Said His Majesty: "Let that reprobate dragon return, if he dares. If he dares, let that reprobate dragon return." The courtiers trembled and gasped: "Pray may the wicked *loong* never return. Never, never return." But little Princess Many Dimples played with her pies and was happy. Her pies had been baked to a queen's taste— or rather to the taste of a princess. Beside the river she worked faithfully in wet white clay. Such beautiful pies. "I do hope that the nice *loong* will return," said Princess Chin Uor. "He is such a fine oven. I shall make a hundred more pies for his baking."

Pie after pie. Even the nurses helped. Instead of saying, "Please, will your Royal Highness not play with this lovely doll?" they said, "Please, is this one rounded enough?" and "Please, shall I scallop the edges a trifle deeper?" and "Shall I imagine that this one contains cherries, or radishes?" or whatever it may be that makers of pies would say in a royal kitchen. So, a hundred pies were made and wheeled to the

177

palace. In reality, they numbered a hundred and one, but the odd one was so thick that it must be called a cake. Howbeit, that is not so important as you might think.

Night followed day—a habit that most nights have. The soldiers slept—as they had been ordered not to do. The hour approached when clock hands point to the highest sky. Midnight came, and with it the mountainous mountain *loong*. Unseen by those whose duty was seeing, the dragon entered King Yang Lang's courtyard. And there he was perplexed and he paused. The King's door was a hodgepodge of magic signs, plastered with yellow paper. Vain to think of entering there. The Queen's door was upside down—best charm of all. To think of entering was vain. The door that led to Princess Chin Uor's sleeping chamber was written thick with words to still a dragon's heart, circles to dizzy his head. Say what you please, the witches and wizards had done good work upon that door. Their charms were written with clearness and force. The *loong* dared not take a second glance. He felt his limbs grow weak. Wisely hastened he from the spell-guarded threshold.

Now in the reign of the Emperor Ming, a crazed and knavish fellow, known to the world as Wing Dow, invented a contrivance called by him "Look-through-the-wall," but which we of today call a "Window." His invention gave the Emperor Ming a severe cold, and Wing Dow came within a sword's width of losing his ears, a story we will not tell now. Here it is necessary to say only that Look-through-the-walls became popular, and many such were to be found in King Yang Lang's palace. In the Princess Chin Uor's room were many wing-dows (or windows), and—hard to believe—those wing-dows were unguarded either by charm or by apple wood beam, which is as good as a charm. Could the dragon pass

178

by such a fine chance? Could he pass the wing-dow and not have a try? When he had come with purpose to do harm? It is easy to imagine the thing that happened. And yet not so easy as it may seem.

The dragon's lumpish head entered the wing-dow. His deer horns, his rabbit eyes, his snake tongue, all entered, and easily enough. A ponderous sofa-cushion foot he placed upon the window ledge. . . .

Crash, and smash, and clatter. . . .

The nurses awoke and screamed, "Save us."

The Princess Chin Uor awoke and said, "Shoo."

Soldiers in the courtyard awoke and lighted green fires as they smote their drums, saying: "Come if you dare. Help. Help."

The dragon was already awake—awake to the danger. Promptly he vanished. Such noise he could not abide.

King Yang Lang came with a golden torch. Greatly he was pleased that the *loong* had been routed.

But Princess Chin Uor was far from pleased. Indeed, she was fretful. From the floor she took a sliver of flint-hard clay. "My pies are all broken. All. All are broken," mourned Princess Many Dimples. "I have placed

them in the wing-dow. And the dragon knocked them down and broke them." And beyond doubt so had he done. There were the pieces.

Still the King remained cheerful. His little daughter's sadness passed unnoticed. His Majesty said: "Your pies, my daughter, are excellent food—let no one deny it—but even better are they to give warning of the dragon's nearness. Your pies have provided me with a wonderful idea. Hereafter we need have no more fear of the *loong*. . . . Ho! General! Awaken your soldiers again. Let them march to the river."

For a week the King's army did no other labor than make mud pies. And like it. The pies were given heat in giant ovens, were baked into stony hardness. Then they were placed throughout the palace, in windows, upon tables, chairs, upon chests and shelves, high and low and everywhere. Even on the chimney tops were rows of glistening pies. The slightest misstep by a prowling dragon would have caused a din most tremendous.

The royal dining table was a shining whiteness, covered with mud pies. So numerous were the pies of the princess that no room remained for food. But that was no cause for worry. The King merely ordered that his rice be placed upon a baked clay pie. Mandarins who visited the palace were much surprised at what they saw—a King eating from common clay. Nevertheless, their own tables were soon covered with Princess Chin Uor's pies. For the King, of course, set all fashions.

And so, we modern peoples speak of our plates and cups and saucers as "China." China? Is it? Yes, and no. China is merely our way of pronouncing Chin Uor. Our plates are merely thin copies of Princess Chin Uor's pies.

180

THIS history tells of the wanderings of Ulysses and his followers in their return from Troy, after the destruction of that famous city of Asia by the Grecians. He was inflamed with a desire of seeing again, after a ten years' absence, his wife and native country Ithaca. He was king of a barren spot, and a poor country, in comparison of the fruitful plains of Asia which he was leaving, or the wealthy kingdoms which he touched upon his return; yet wherever he came, he could never see a soil which appeared in his eyes half so sweet or desirable as his country earth. This made him refuse the offers of the goddess Calypso to stay with her, and partake of her immortality, in the delightful island; and this gave him strength to break from the enchantments of Circe, the daughter of the Sun.

The Cyclops

RETOLD BY CHARLES LAMB

Illustrated by Hans A. Mueller

From Troy ill winds cast Ulysses and his fleet upon the coast of the Cicons, a people hostile to the Grecians. Landing his forces, he laid siege to the chief city Ismarus, which he took, and with it much spoil, and slew many people.

But success proved fatal to him; for his soldiers, elated with the spoil, and the good store of provisions which they found in that place, fell to eating and drinking, forgetful of their safety, till the Cicons, who inhabited the coast, had time to assemble their friends and allies from the interior, who, mustering in prodigious force, set upon the Grecians, while they negligently reveled and feasted, and slew many of them and recovered the spoil. They, dispirited and thinned in their numbers, with difficulty made their retreat good to the ships.

Thence they set sail, sad at heart, yet something cheered that, with such fearful odds against them, they had not all been utterly destroyed. A dreadful tempest ensued, which for two nights and two days tossed them about, but the third day the weather cleared, and they had hopes of a favorable gale to carry them to Ithaca; but as they doubled the Cape of Malea, suddenly a north wind arising drove them back as far as Cythera.

After that, for the space of nine days, contrary winds continued to drive them in an opposite direction to the point to which they were bound, and the tenth day they put in at a shore where a race of men dwell that are sustained by the fruit of the lotos tree.

Here Ulysses sent some of his men to land for fresh water, who were met by certain of the inhabitants, that gave them some of their country's food to eat; not with any ill intention towards them, though in the event it proved pernicious; for, having eaten of this fruit, so pleasant it proved to their appetite that they in a minute quite forgot all thoughts of home, or of their countrymen, or of ever returning back to the ships to give an account of what sort of inhabitants dwelt there, but they would needs stay and live there among them and eat of that precious food forever; and when Ulysses sent other of his men to look for them, and to bring them back by force, they strove, and wept, and would not leave their food for heaven itself, so much the pleasure of that enchanting food had bewitched them.

But Ulysses caused them to be bound hand and foot, and cast under the hatches; and set sail with all possible speed

from that baneful coast, lest others after them might taste the lotos, which had such strange qualities to make men forget their native country and the thoughts of home.

Coasting on all that night by unknown and out-of-the-way shores, they came by day-break to the land where the Cyclops dwell, a sort of giant shepherds that neither sow nor plough, but the earth untilled produces for them rich wheat and barley and grapes, yet they have neither bread nor wine, nor know the arts of cultivation, nor care to know them: for they live each man to himself, without laws or government, or anything like a state of kingdom, but their dwellings are in caves, on the steep heads of mountains, every man's household governed by his own caprice, or not governed at all, their wives and children as lawless as themselves, none caring for others, but each doing as he or she thinks good. Ships or boats they have none, nor artificers to make them, no trade or commerce, or wish to visit other shores; yet they have convenient places for harbors and for shipping.

Here Ulysses with a chosen party of twelve followers landed, to explore what sort of men dwelt there, whether hospitable and friendly to strangers, or altogether wild and savage, for as yet no dwellers appeared in sight.

The first sign of habitation which they came to was a giant's cave rudely fashioned, but of a size which betokened the vast proportions of its owner, the pillars which supported it being the bodies of huge oaks or pines, in the natural state of the tree, and all about showed more marks of strength than skill in whoever built it.

Ulysses, entering in, admired the savage contrivances and artless structure of the place, and longed to see the tenant of so outlandish a mansion; but well conjecturing that gifts would have more avail in extracting courtesy than strength would succeed in forcing it, from such a one as he expected to find the inhabitant, he resolved to flatter his hospitality with a present of Greek wine, of which he had store in twelve great vessels; so strong that no one ever drank it without an infusion of twenty parts of water to one of wine, yet the fragrance of it even then was so delicious that it would have vexed a man who smelled it to abstain from tasting it; but whoever tasted it was able to raise his courage to the height of heroic deeds.

Taking with them a goatskin flagon full of this precious liquor, they ventured into the recesses of the cave. Here they pleased themselves a whole day with beholding the giant's kitchen, where the flesh of sheep and goats lay strewn; his dairy where goat-milk stood ranged in troughs and pails, his pens where he kept his live animals, but these he had driven forth to pasture with him when he went out in the morning.

While they were feasting their eyes with a sight of these

curiosities, their ears were suddenly deafened with a noise like the falling of a house. It was the owner of the cave, who had been abroad all day feeding his flock, as his custom was, in the mountains, and now drove them home in the evening from pasture. He threw down a pile of firewood, which he had been gathering against supper time, before the mouth of the cave, which occasioned the crash they heard.

The Grecians hid themselves in the remote parts of the cave at sight of the uncouth monster. It was Polyphemus, the largest and savagest of the Cyclops, who boasted himself to be the son of Neptune. He looked more like a mountain crag than a man, and to his brutal body he had a brutish mind answerable.

He drove his flock, all that gave milk, to the interior of the cave, but left the rams and the he-goats without. Then taking up a stone so massy that twenty oxen could not have drawn it, he placed it at the mouth of the cave, to defend the entrance, and sat him down to milk his ewes and his goats; which done, he lastly kindled a fire, and throwing his great eye round the cave (for the Cyclops have no more than one eye, and that placed in the midst of their forehead), by the glimmering light he discerned some of Ulysses's men.

"Ho! guests, what are you? merchants or wandering thieves?" he bellowed out in a voice which took from them all power of reply, it was so astounding.

Only Ulysses summoned resolution to answer, that they came neither for plunder nor traffic, but were Grecians who had lost their way, returning from Troy; which famous city, under the conduct of Agamemnon, the renowned son of Atreus, they had sacked, and laid level with the ground.

Yet now they prostrated themselves humbly before his feet, whom they acknowledged to be mightier than they, and

185

besought him that he would bestow the rites of hospitality upon them, for that Jove was the avenger of wrongs done to strangers, and would fiercely resent any injury which they might suffer.

"Fool," said the Cyclops, "to come so far to preach to me the fear of the gods. We Cyclops care not for your Jove, whom you fable to be nursed by a goat, nor any of your blessed ones. We are stronger than they, and dare bid open battle to Jove himself, though you and all your fellows of the earth join with him." And he bade them tell him where their ship was, in which they came, and whether they had any companions.

But Ulysses, with wise caution, made answer that they had no ship or companions, but were unfortunate men whom the sea, splitting their ship in pieces, had dashed upon his coast, and they alone had escaped.

The Cyclops replied nothing, but gripping two of the nearest of them, as if they had been no more than children, he dashed their brains out against the earth, and (shocking to relate) tore in pieces their limbs, and devoured them, yet warm and trembling, making a lion's meal of them, lapping the blood: for the Cyclops are man-eaters, and esteem human flesh to be a delicacy far above goat's or kid's; though by reason of their abhorred customs few men approach their coast except some stragglers, or now and then a shipwrecked mariner. At a sight so horrid Ulysses and his men were like distracted people. The Cyclops, when he had made an end of his wicked supper, drained a draught of goat's milk down his prodigious throat, and lay down and slept among his goats.

Then Ulysses drew his sword, and half resolved to thrust it with all his might in at the bosom of the sleeping monster; but wiser thoughts restrained him, else they had there with-

186

out help all perished, for none but Polyphemus himself could have removed that mass of stone which he had placed to guard the entrance. So they were constrained to abide all that night in fear.

When day came Cyclops awoke, and kindling a fire, made his breakfast of two other of his unfortunate prisoners, then milked his goats as he was accustomed, and pushing aside the vast stone, and shutting it again, when he had done, upon the prisoners, with as much ease as a man opens and shuts a quiver's lid, he let out his flock, and drove them before him with whistlings (as sharp as winds in storms) to the mountains.

Then Ulysses, of whose strength or cunning the Cyclops seems to have had as little heed as of an infant's, being left alone, with the remnant of his men which the Cyclops had not devoured, gave manifest proof how far manly wisdom excels brutish force. He chose a stake from among the wood which the Cyclops had piled up for firing, in length and thickness like a mast, which he sharpened and hardened in the fire, and selected four men, and instructed them what they should do with this stake, and made them perfect in their parts.

When the evening was come, the Cyclops drove home his sheep; and as fortune directed it, either of purpose, or that his memory was overruled by the gods to his hurt (as in the issue it proved), he drove the males of his flock, contrary to his custom, along with the dams into the pens. Then shutting-to the stone of the cave, he fell to his horrible supper. When he had despatched two more of the Grecians, Ulysses waxed bold with the contemplation of his project, and took a bowl of Greek wine, and merrily dared the Cyclops to drink.

"Cyclops," he said, "take a bowl of wine from the hand of your guest: it may serve to digest the man's flesh that you

188

have eaten, and show what drink our ship held before it went down. All I ask in recompense, if you find it good, is to be dismissed in a whole skin. Truly you must look to have few visitors, if you observe this new custom of eating your guests."

The brute took and drank, and vehemently enjoyed the taste of wine, which was new to him, and swilled again at the flagon, and entreated for more, and prayed Ulysses to tell him his name, that he might bestow a gift upon the man who had given him such brave liquor. The Cyclops (he said) had grapes, but this rich juice (he swore) was simply divine.

Again Ulysses plied him with the wine, and the fool drank it as fast as it was poured out; and again he asked the name of his benefactor, which Ulysses, cunningly dissembling, said, "My name is Noman: my kindred and friends in my own country call me Noman."

"Then," said the Cyclop, "this is the kindness I will show thee, Noman: I will eat thee last of all thy friends."

He had scarce expressed his savage kindness, when the fumes of the strong wine overcame him, and he reeled down upon the floor and sank into a dead sleep.

Ulysses watched his time, while the monster lay insensible, and heartening up his men, they placed the sharp end of the stake in the fire till it was heated red-hot, and some god gave them a courage beyond that which they were used to have, and the four men with difficulty bored the sharp end of the huge stake, which they had heated red-hot, right into the eye of the drunken cannibal, and Ulysses helped to thrust it in with all his might, still further and further, with effort, as men bore with an auger, till the scalded blood gushed out, and the eyeball smoked, and the strings of the eye cracked, as the burning rafter broke in it, and the eye hissed, as hot iron hisses when it is plunged into water.

He, waking, roared with the pain so loud that all the cavern broke into claps like thunder. They fled, and dispersed into corners. He plucked the burning stake from his eye, and hurled the wood madly about the cave. Then he cried out with a mighty voice for his brethren the Cyclops, that dwelt hard by in caverns upon hills; they, hearing the terrible shout, came flocking from all parts to inquire what ailed Polyphemus? and what cause he had for making such horrid clamors in the nighttime to break their sleeps? if his fright proceeded from any mortal? if strength or craft had given him his death's blow?

He made answer from within that Noman had hurt him, Noman had killed him, Noman was with him in the cave.

They replied, "If no man has hurt thee, and no man is with thee, then thou art alone, and the evil that afflicts thee is from the hand of heaven, which none can resist or help." So they left him and went their way, thinking that some disease troubled him.

He, blind and ready to split with the anguish of the pain, went groaning up and down in the dark, to find the doorway, which when he found, he removed the stone, and sat in the threshold, feeling if he could lay hold on any man going out with the sheep, which (the day now breaking) were beginning to issue forth to their accustomed pastures.

But Ulysses, whose first artifice in giving himself that ambiguous name had succeeded so well with the Cyclops, was not of a wit so gross to be caught by that palpable device. But casting about in his mind all the ways which he could contrive for escape (no less than all their lives depending on the success), at last he thought of this expedient. He made knots of the osier twigs upon which the Cyclops commonly slept, with which he tied the fattest and fleeciest of the rams

190

together, three in a rank, and under the middle ram he tied a man, and himself last, wrapping himself fast with both his hands in the rich wool of one, the fairest of the flock.

And now the sheep began to issue forth very fast, the males went first, the females unmilked stood by, bleating and requiring the hand of their shepherd in vain to milk them. Still as the males passed, he felt the backs of those fleecy fools, never dreaming that they carried his enemies under them: so they passed on till the last ram came loaded with his wool and Ulysses together.

He stopped that ram and felt him, and had his hand once in the hair of Ulysses, yet knew it not, and he chid the ram for being last, and spoke to it as if it understood him, and asked it whether it did not wish that its master had his eye again, which that abominable Noman with his execrable rout had put out, when they had got him down with wine; and he

willed the ram to tell him whereabouts in the cave his enemy lurked, that he might dash his brains and strew them about, to ease his heart of that tormenting revenge which rankled in it. After a deal of such foolish talk to the beast he let it go.

When Ulysses found himself free, he let go his hold, and assisted in disengaging his friends. The rams which had befriended them they carried off with them to the ships, where their companions with tears in their eyes received them, as men escaped from death.

They plied their oars, and set their sails, and when they were got as far off from shore as a voice would reach, Ulysses cried out to the Cyclops: "Cyclops, thou should'st not have so much abused thy monstrous strength as to devour thy guests. Jove, by my hand, sends thee requital to pay thy savage inhumanity."

The Cyclops heard, and came forth enraged and in his anger he plucked a fragment of a rock and threw it with blind fury at the ships: it narrowly escaped lighting upon the bark in which Ulysses sat, but with the fall it raised so fierce an ebb as bore back the ship till it almost touched the shore.

"Cyclops," said Ulysses, "if any ask thee who imposed on thee that unsightly blemish in thine eye, say it was Ulysses, son of Laertes: the king of Ithaca am I called, the waster of cities."

Then they crowded sail, and beat the old sea, and forth they went with a forward gale; sad for forepast losses, yet glad to have escaped at any rate; till they came to the isle where Aeolus reigned, who is god of the winds.

Here Ulysses and his men were courteously received by the monarch, who showed him his twelve children which have rule over the twelve winds. A month they stayed and feasted with him, and at the end of the month he dismissed

192

them with many presents, and gave to Ulysses at parting an ox's hide, in which were enclosed all the winds: only he left abroad the western wind, to play upon their sails and waft them gently home to Ithaca. This bag, bound in a glittering silver band, so close that no breath could escape, Ulysses hung up at the mast. His companions did not know its contents, but guessed that the monarch had given to him some treasures of gold or silver.

Nine days they sailed smoothly, favored by the western wind, and by the tenth they approached so nigh as to discern lights kindled on the shores of their country earth: when by ill fortune, Ulysses, overcome with the fatigue of watching the helm, fell asleep.

The mariners seized the opportunity, and one of them said to the rest: "A fine time has this leader of ours: wherever he goes he is sure of presents, when we come away empty-handed; and see what King Aeolus has given him, store no doubt of gold and silver!"

A word was enough to those covetous wretches, who quick as thought untied the bag, and instead of gold, out rushed with mighty noise all the winds.

Ulysses awoke with the noise and saw their mistake, but too late, for the ship was driving with all the winds back far from Ithaca, far as to the island of Aeolus from which they had parted, in one hour measuring back what in nine days they had scarcely tracked, and in sight of home too! Up he flew amazed and raving, doubted whether he should not fling himself into the sea for grief of his bitter disappointment.

At last he hid himself under the hatches for shame. And scarce could he be prevailed upon, when he was told he was arrived again in the harbor of King Aeolus, to go himself or send to that monarch for a second succor; so much the dis-

193

grace of having misused his royal bounty (though it was the crime of his followers and not his own) weighed upon him: and when at last he went, and took a herald with him, and came where the god sat on his throne, feasting with his children, he would not thrust in among them at their meat, but sat himself down like one unworthy in the threshold.

Indignation seized Aeolus to behold him in that manner returned; and he said, "Ulysses, what has brought you back? Are you so soon tired of your country? Or did not our present please you? We thought we had given you a kingly passport."

Ulysses made answer, "My men have done this ill mischief to me: they did it while I slept."

"Wretch," said Aeolus, "avaunt, and quit our shores: it fits not us to convoy men whom the gods hate, and will have perish."

Forth they sailed, but with far different hopes than when they left the same harbor the first time with all the winds confined, only the west wind suffered to play upon their sails to waft them in gentle murmers to Ithaca. They were now the sport of every gale that blew, and despaired of ever seeing home more. Now those covetous mariners were cured of their surfeit for gold, and would not have touched it if it had lain in untold heaps before them.

Six days and nights they drove along, and on the seventh day they put into Lamos, a port of the Laestrygonians. So spacious this harbor was that it held with ease all their fleet, which rode at anchor, safe from any storms, all but the ship in which Ulysses was embarked. He, as if prophetic of the mischance which followed, kept still without the harbor, making fast his bark to a rock at the land's point, which he climbed with purpose to survey the country. He saw a city with smoke ascending from the roofs, but neither ploughs going nor oxen

194

yoked, nor any sign of agricultural works. Making choice of two men, he sent them to the city to explore what sort of inhabitants dwelt there.

His messengers had not gone far before they met a damsel, of stature surpassing human, who was coming to draw water from a spring. They asked her who dwelt in that land. She made no reply but led them in silence to her father's palace. He was a monarch and named Antiphas. He and all his people were giants.

When they entered the palace, a woman, the mother of the damsel, but far taller than she, rushed abroad and called for Antiphas. He came, and snatching up one of the two men, made as if he would devour him. The other fled. Antiphas raised a mighty shout, and instantly, this way and that, multitudes of gigantic people issued out at the gates, and making for the harbor, tore up huge pieces of the rocks, and flung them at the ships which lay there, all which they utterly overwhelmed and sank; and the unfortunate bodies of men which floated, and which the sea did not devour, these cannibals thrust through with harpoons, like fishes, and bore them off to their dire feast.

Ulysses with his single bark that had never entered the harbor escaped; that bark which was now the only vessel left of all the gallant navy that had set sail with him from Troy. He pushed off from the shore, cheering the sad remnant of his men, whom horror at the sight of their countrymen's fate had almost turned to marble.

STAFF in hand and wallet on back, Tyll fared through the land and came to Brunswick. The sharp March wind tried mightily to go through his very body and Tyll tried just as hard to find shelter to protect it. It was a close race between the two.

One day he was in the inn where the bakers came to gossip and drink. There he met a master baker who told him he looked like a monkey dragged from the mire, and asked whether his profession was teaching songs to the owls. The fellow was known as a jester and Tyll looked so woebegone that the baker thought he would have some sport with him.

Bake Monkeys and Owls and the Baker Growls

BY M. JAGENDORF

Illustrated by Fritz Eichenber

"No," replied Tyll, "I was helper to a baker who liked to sleep behind the oven."

"Well, I am not lazy, but I need a baker to work in my shop."

So the bargain was closed, and Tyll went to the baker's home, where he was sheltered from wind and weather.

Soon Tyll found the baker putting all the hard work on him, while spending his own nights at the inn. The very second night his new master said to him:

"You will do all the baking in the night and I will help you in the morning." Now, you know that most of the baking is done during the night.

Tyll replied innocently.

"What shall I bake, good master?"

This made the baker angry and he replied mockingly:

"You are a baker and ask me what to bake? Ho, ho, ho! What did you bake before? I suppose big-eyed owls and long-tailed monkeys. Well, try the same here. Try it here, my smart fellow!" He walked out, still laughing mockingly.

Tyll laughed, too, and began to work. He took the dough and kneaded it into fat owls and skinny owls, tall owls and short owls; he made dough monkeys with long tails and short faces and long faces with stumpy tails; in short, instead of rolls and bread and cake, he made over a hundred monkeys and owls of every shape and size. These he baked brown and crisp. Just as he was taking them out of the oven, which was about the time when gray cats come home from caroling the stars, the baker came in. He stood speechless at the sight.

"Caitiff! Have you lost your mind? Mangy vagabond! What have you done? Where are the white rolls, the little breads and cakes I ordered you to bake?"

"I baked exactly what you ordered me to bake. Didn't you tell me to make big-eyed owls and long-tailed monkeys? That's exactly what I did."

"O fool of fools! Witless donkey! What shall I do with these? I can't sell them. Now, you pay for the dough or I'll put you in prison."

"I'll pay for the dough," Tyll replied, "but then these dough-animals belong to me."

"Take these owls and monkeys who look like you and give them to those who are your brothers."

Tyll paid the money, took them and went to the market place. It was the day before St. Nicholas day and he thought it would be easy to sell the funny-looking rolls and cakes to the children.

He was not wrong. A great crowd came around to look at the strange merchandise and soon he had a good trade, selling his strangely shaped cakes at a much higher price than he could have those of ordinary shape.

The baker passed and saw what he saw, which added fuel to his fury.

"Pay me for the wood and the hire of the oven," he cried.

"A bargain made is a bargain closed," replied Tyll merrily.

The baker ran to the judges, and Tyll, smelling trouble, ran the other way. So when the bailiff came he was gone where the owls are during the day and the moles are during the night, and none could find him.

198

Now it was told before how two hundred pounds were set upon Robin Hood's head. It is now to be told how the Sheriff of Nottingham swore that he himself would bring Robin Hood to justice, and for two reasons: first, because he wanted the two hundred pounds, and next, because the forester that Robin Hood had killed was of kin to him.

But the Sheriff knew what a force Robin had about him in Sherwood, and that he could not serve a warrant for his arrest as he could upon another man that had broken the laws; therefore he was compelled to devise some cunning trick wherewith to entrap bold Robin.

Thus thinking the Sheriff said to himself, "This Robin Hood hath a daring soul. If I could but persuade him nigh to Nottingham Town so that I could lay hand upon him, he would never get away again." Then it came to him that were he to proclaim a great shooting-match and offer some grand prize, Robin Hood might be over-persuaded by his spirit to

The Shooting-Match at Nottingham Town

BY HOWARD PYLE

Illustrated by Howard Pyle

come to the butts. Accordingly he sent messengers north and south, and east and west, to proclaim through town, hamlet, and countryside, this grand shooting-match, and everyone was bidden who could draw a long bow, and the prize was to be an arrow of pure beaten gold.

When Robin Hood first heard the news of this he was in Lincoln Town, and hastening back to Sherwood Forest he soon called all his merry men about him and spoke to them thus:

"Now hearken, my merry men all, to the news that I have brought from Lincoln Town to-day. Our friend the Sheriff of Nottingham hath proclaimed a shooting-match, and hath sent messengers to tell of it through all the countryside, and the prize is to be a bright, golden arrow. Now I fain would have one of us win it, both because of the fairness of the prize and because our sweet friend the Sheriff hath offered it. So we will take our bows and shafts and go there to shoot, for I know right well that merriment will be a-going. Some of you shall clothe yourselves as curtal friars, and some as rustic peasants, and some as tinkers, or as beggars, but see that each man taketh a good bow or broadsword, in case need should arise. As for myself, I will shoot for this same golden arrow, and should I win it, we will hang it to the branches of our good greenwood tree for the joy of all the band. How like you the plan, my merry men all?"

Then "Good! Good!" cried all the band right heartily.

A fair sight was Nottingham Town on the day of the shooting-match. All along upon the green meadow beneath the town wall stretched a row of benches, one above the other, whereon sat knight and lady, squire and dame, and rich burghers and their wives. At the end of the range, near the target, was a raised seat bedecked with ribbons and scarfs and garlands of flowers, where sat the Sheriff of Nottingham and his dame. The range was two-score paces broad. At one end stood the target; at the other a tent of striped canvas, from the pole of which fluttered many-colored flags and streamers.

Then the herald stood forth and loudly proclaimed the rules of the game as follows:

200

"Shoot each man from yon mark, which is sevenscore yards and ten from the target. One arrow shooteth each man first, and from all the archers shall the ten that shoot the fairest shafts be chosen for to shoot again. Two arrows shooteth each man of these ten, then shall the three that shoot the fairest shafts be chosen for to shoot again. Three arrows shooteth each man of those three, and to him that shooteth the fairest shafts shall the prize be given."

Then the Sheriff leaned forward, looking keenly among the press of archers to find whether Robin Hood was amongst them; but no one was there clad in Lincoln green, such as was worn by Robin and his band. "Nevertheless," said the Sheriff to himself, "he may still be there, and I miss him among the crowd of other men. But let me see when but ten men shoot, for I wot he will be among the ten, or I know him not."

And now the archers shot, each man in turn, and the good folk never saw such archery as was done that day. Six arrows were within the clout, four within the black, and only two smote the outer ring; so that when the last arrow sped and struck the target, all the people shouted aloud, for it was noble shooting.

And now but ten men were left of all those that had shot before, and of these ten, six were famous throughout the land, and most of the folk gathered there knew them. These six men were Gilbert o' the Red Cap, Adam o' the Dell, Diccon Cruikshank, William o' Leslie, Hubert o' Cloud, and Swithin o' Hertford. Two others were yeomen of merry Yorkshire, another was a tall stranger in blue, who said he came from London Town, and the last was a tattered stranger in scarlet, who wore a patch over one eye.

"Now," quoth the Sheriff to a man-at-arms who stood near him, "seest thou Robin Hood amongst those ten?"

"Nay, that do I not, your worship," answered the man. "Six of them I know right well. Of those Yorkshire yeomen, one is too tall and the other too short, for that bold knave. Robin's beard is as yellow as gold, while yon tattered beggar in scarlet hath a beard of brown, besides being blind of one eye. As for the stranger in blue, Robin's shoulders, I ween, are three inches broader than his."

"Then," quoth the Sheriff, smiting his thigh angrily, "yon knave is a coward as well as a rogue, and dares not show his face among good men and true."

Then, after they had rested a short time, those ten stout men stepped forth to shoot again. Each man shot two arrows, and as they shot, not a word was spoken, but all the crowd

202

watched with scarce a breath of sound; but when the last had shot his arrow, another great shout arose, while many cast their caps aloft for joy of such marvellous shooting.

And now but three men were left of all those that had shot before. One was Gill o' the Red Cap, one the tattered stranger in scarlet, and one Adam o' the Dell of Tamworth Town. Then all the people called aloud, some crying, "Ho for Gilbert o' the Red Cap!" and some, "Hey for stout Adam o' Tamworth!" but not a single man in the crowd called upon the stranger in scarlet.

"Now, shoot thou well, Gilbert," cried the Sheriff, "and if thine be the best shaft, fivescore broad silver pennies will I give to thee besides the prize."

"Truly I will do my best," quoth Gilbert, right sturdily. "A man cannot do aught but his best, but that will I strive to do this day." So saying, he drew forth a fair smooth arrow with a broad feather and fitted it deftly to the string, then drawing his bow with care he sped the shaft. Straight flew the arrow and lit fairly in the clout, a finger breadth from the center. "A Gilbert, a Gilbert!" shouted all the crowd; and, "Now, by my faith," cried the Sheriff, smiting his hands together, "that is a shrewd shot."

Then the tattered stranger stepped forth, and all the people laughed as they saw a yellow patch that showed beneath his arm when he raised his elbow to shoot, and also to see him aim with but one eye. He drew the good yew bow quickly, and quickly loosed a shaft; so short was the time that no man could draw a breath betwixt the drawing and the shooting; yet his arrow lodged nearer the center than the other by twice the length of a barley-corn.

"Now by all the saints in Paradise!" cried the Sheriff, "that is a lovely shaft in very truth!"

203

Then Adam o' the Dell shot, carefully and cautiously, and his arrow lodged close beside the stranger's. Then after a short space they all three shot again, and once more each arrow lodged within the clout, but this time Adam o' the Dell's was farthest from the center, and again the tattered stranger's shot was the best. Then, after another time of rest, they all shot for the third time. This time Gilbert took great heed to his aim, keenly measuring the distance and shooting with shrewdest care. Straight flew the arrow, and all shouted till the very flags that waved in the breeze shook with the sound, and the rooks and daws flew clamoring about the roofs of the old gray tower, for the shaft had lodged close beside the spot that marked the very center.

"Well done, Gilbert!" cried the Sheriff, right joyously. "Fain am I to believe the prize is thine, and right fairly won. Now, thou ragged knave, let me see thee shoot a better shaft than that."

Naught spake the stranger but took his place, while all was hushed, and no one spoke or even seemed to breathe, so great was the silence for wonder what he would do. Meanwhile, also, quite still stood the stranger holding his bow in his hand, while one could count five; then he drew his trusty yew, holding it drawn but a moment, then loosed the string. Straight flew the arrow, and so true that it smote a gray goose feather from off Gilbert's shaft, which fell fluttering through the sunlit air as the stranger's arrow lodged close beside his of the Red Cap, and in the very center. No one spoke a word for a while and no one shouted, but each man looked into his neighbor's face amazedly.

"Nay," quoth old Adam o' the Dell presently, drawing a long breath and shaking his head as he spoke, "twoscore years and more have I shot shaft, and maybe not all times bad, but I shoot no more this day, for no man can match with yon

204

stranger, whosoe'er he may be." Then he thrust his shaft into his quiver, rattling, and unstrung his bow without another word.

Then the Sheriff came down from his dais and drew near, in all his silks and velvets, to where the tattered stranger stood leaning upon his stout bow, whilst the good folk crowded around to see the man who shot so wondrously well. "Here, good fellow," quoth the Sheriff, "take thou the prize, and well and fairly hast thou won it, I trow. What may be thy name, and whence comest thou?"

"Men do call me Jock o' Teviotdale, and thence am I come," said the stranger.

"Then, by Our Lady, Jock, thou art the fairest archer that e'er mine eyes beheld, and if thou wilt join my service I will clothe thee with a better coat than that thou hast upon thy back; thou shalt eat and drink of the best, and at every Christmas-tide fourscore marks shall be thy wage. I trow thou drawest better bow than that same coward knave, Robin Hood, that dared not show his face here this day. Say, good fellow, wilt thou join my service?"

"Nay, that will I not," quoth the stranger, roughly. "I will be mine own, and no man in all merry England shall be my master."

"Then get thee gone, and a murrain seize thee!" cried the Sheriff, and his voice trembled with anger. "And by my faith and troth I have a good part of a mind to have thee beaten for thine insolence!" Then he turned upon his heel and strode away.

It was a right motley company that gathered about the noble greenwood tree in Sherwood's depths that same day. A score and more of barefoot friars were there, and some that looked like tinkers, and some that seemed to be sturdy beggars and rustic hinds; and seated upon a mossy couch was one all clad in tattered scarlet, with a patch over one eye; and in his hand he held the golden arrow that was the prize of the great shooting-match. Then, amidst a noise of talking and laughter, he took the patch from off his eye and stripped away the scarlet rags from off his body and showed himself all clothed in fair Lincoln green, and quoth he: "Easy come these things away, but walnut stain cometh not so speedily from yellow hair." Then all laughed louder than before for it was Robin Hood himself that had won the prize from the Sheriff's very hands.

"By my troth," said the Sheriff, as he sat at meat in the great hall of his house at Nottingham Town, "I did reckon full roundly that that knave, Robin Hood, would be at the game to-day. I did not think that he was such a coward. But who could that saucy knave be who answered me to my beard so bravely?"

Then, even as he finished speaking, something fell rattling among the dishes on the table, while those that sat near started up wondering what it might be. After a while one of the men-at-arms gathered courage enough to pick it up and bring it to the Sheriff. Then everyone saw that it was a blunted gray goose shaft, with a fine scroll, about the thickness of a goose quill, tied near to its head. The Sheriff opened the scroll and glanced at it, while the veins upon his forehead swelled and his cheeks grew ruddy with rage as he read, for this was what he saw:

"Now Heaven bless thy grace this day,
Say all in sweet Sherwood,
For thou didst give the prize away
To merry Robin Hood."

THE lively fancy of your young minds will find no difficulty in following me from tropic climes to lands of ice and snow. Your wits and mine will run a rapid pace with neither fall nor doubting stumble.

My adventures have been varied as also have been the excursions of your adventurous imaginations. Therefore, I once set off from Rome on a journey to Russia in the midst of winter. I had a notion that frost and snow must, of course, improve the roads which every traveler had described as uncommonly bad through the northern parts of Germany, Poland, Courland, and Livonia. I went on horseback, as the least difficult manner of traveling. I was but lightly clothed and suffered greatly the more I advanced to the northeast. On my way I came upon a poor old man lying, shivering and lifeless, by the roadside. Scarcely a garment had he wherewith to cover his aged body. What must not the poor soul have suffered? Though I felt the severity of the weather myself, I pitied the poor creature and threw my cloak over him, and immediately I heard a voice of approval blessing me for that act of charity, saying: "For this you will be rewarded, my son, in good time."

The Travels of Baron Munchausen

RETOLD BY JOHN MARTIN

Illustrated by Gustave Doré

Onward I pursued my journey; night and darkness overtook me. No village was to be seen. The country was covered with snow, and I was unacquainted with the road.

Exceedingly weary, I alighted and fastened my horse to

something that looked like a pointed stump of a tree which stood up above the snow. For the sake of safety I placed my pistols under my arms and lay down upon the snow, where I slept so soundly that I did not open my eyes till full daylight. Even you will not easily understand my astonishment to find myself lying in a churchyard in the midst of a village. My horse was not to be seen, but presently I heard him neigh somewhere above me. On looking upwards, I saw him hanging by his bridle to the weathercock of the church steeple.

My changed locality and the strange position of my horse were at first bewildering if not mysterious, but matters were soon very plain to me. The village had been covered with a heavy fall of snow. While I slept, a sudden change of weather had taken place, and the snow had melted. Slowly and gently I was lowered to the level of the churchyard; and what in the dark I had taken to be a stump of a little tree above the snow proved to have been the top of the church weathercock. There hung my horse, high in the air.

Without thinking long, I took one of my pistols, shot the bridle in two, brought down the horse, and without further ado proceeded on my journey. (Here the Baron seems to have entirely lost his tender feelings for those in suffering or want. Certainly a good breakfast of corn for his horse, who had fasted so long and hung so high, would have been in keeping with the charitable deeds of which, but the night before, the Baron bravely boasted.)

My noble beast carried me well, advancing into the interior of Russia. I found going on horseback in those parts rather unfashionable in winter; therefore, I yielded, as I always do, to the customs of the country, took a single-horse sleigh, and drove briskly towards Saint Petersburg.

I do not exactly remember at the moment whether it was

in Eastland or Jugemanland, but I do know that in the midst
of a dreary forest I spied a terrible wolf making after me with
all the speed of ravenous winter hunger. He soon overtook

me. There was no way of escape. Without thought, I laid myself down flat in the sleigh, and let my horse run for our safety. The means of escape I wished, but hardly hoped for or expected, happened immediately.

The wolf did not mind me in the least, but took a leap over me, falling furiously on my poor horse and beginning instantly to devour the animal. It was but natural that the horse ran the faster in anxious desire to escape a foe attacking so savagely from the rear. Being unnoticed and entirely safe myself, I lifted my head up slyly and with surprise beheld that the wolf had already half eaten my wildly galloping horse. So great was my horror and indignation that I fell upon him with the butt end of my whip. This unexpected attack from the rear frightened the creature so much that he leaped forward with all his might and hastily bolted the still undevoured half of my horse. In so doing, he had, of course, eaten his way into my beast's harness and found himself being properly drubbed by his new master. At a speed unknown in these parts, we arrived in full career in Saint Petersburg, each in a manner unexpected, and much to the astonishment of the many spectators who observed our entry into town.

Thus ended another of my adventures. Though remarkable to those of less eventful lives, I look upon it as of little import compared with others which I shall tell you.

My young Friends have heard, I am sure, of Saint Hubert, the protector of hunters, and also of the noble stag with a cross between his antlers which appeared to him in the forest. If you are not familiar with the good Saint, and would add to your store of sportsman's knowledge, I herewith advise you to look into the Saint's career. Maybe one day you may come upon an adventure worthy of recording, as is the one I shall now tell you.

210

Having once used all my shot, I found myself suddenly in the presence of a stately stag. The creature was looking at me with a calm indifference that seemed to prove that he knew of my empty pouches. But with the usual presence of mind which has served me so well on many occasions, I loaded my gun with a great charge of powder and rammed upon it a handful of cherrystones, for I had sucked the fruit as far as the hurry would permit. Thus I let fly at him and hit him just on the middle of the forehead between the antlers. The shot stunned him. He staggered, but in a moment made off at full speed.

A year or two after, being in the same forest with a hunting party, I beheld a noble stag with a fine full-grown cherry tree more than ten feet high growing out between his wide-spread antlers. I immediately remembered my former adventure and looked upon him as my property. I brought him to the ground by one shot. To the true sportsman comes quick reward in field or wood way; thus my good marksmanship not only brought me a fine haunch of venison, but also an excellent cherry-sauce, for the tree was covered with the richest fruit, the like of which I had never tasted before.

I trust that my young Readers of tender hearts and ready sympathies will not think me a hunter who prided himself in slaughter for glory or gain. You must understand that one of my fine feelings and modesty should not be so misjudged. I will, therefore, tell you of another adventure that might have ended ill for me had I not used my quickness of thought and deftness of imagination. Once, in a Polish forest, daylight and powder were gone.

Returning homeward, a terrible bear made at me in great speed, his eyes flaming with hunger and his jaws wide with the same unreasonable desire. All my pockets were searched in an instant for powder and ball, but in vain. I found nothing but two spare flints used on the hammer of my fowling-piece. My predicament was dreadful and promised but one ending for me, namely, bruin's dinner. Being an athlete and a runner of some renown, I ran, exerting my prowess to the utmost. As I was familiar with the bear's natural awkwardness, I followed no straight course, but dodged and doubled in my hurried ways. In one of my quick turns, the bear stumbled and fell. This gave me the opportunity I sought, and with great strength I hurled one of my flints at the creature's side. So tremendous was the blow that he was turned full around, thus exposing his other side, at which I let drive my second flint. As I had wisely planned, the flints met with direful force in the savage beast's inward parts, struck fire, and blew up the bear with a terrible explosion. Though I came off safe for the time, I should not wish to try it again, or venture against bears with such poor ammunition.

I ofttimes think that my well-known bravery led me into acts of needless danger and a lack of care for my own welfare. The fiercest and most dangerous animals generally came upon me when I was defenseless. They seemed to have a notion or instinct of this on many occasions. Once a frightful wolf rushed upon me so suddenly and so closely that my running served me not at all. There was nothing to do but follow a simple instinct, and that was to catch hold of the nearest and least resisting object at hand. This object happened to be the wolf's tail, which was unusually long and strong. With strength born of terror, I whirled the wolf about my head and continued to do so until I came to a tree limb to which I securely tied the wolf whose tail proved useful in making the most secure knot. There I left him, saying, "The longer you hang, Sir, the more time you will have to repent your rudeness to a gentleman who desired only to return to his home undisturbed."

The same means of self-protection would not have answered against a mad dog, which soon after came running against me in a narrow street of Saint Petersburg. Run, those

who can, I thought; and to do this the better, I threw off my cloak and was soon safe within the doors of my home. I sent my servant for the cloak and he put it in the wardrobe with my other clothes. The day after, I was amazed and frightened by Jack's bawling, "Oh, Master, your fur cloak is mad!" I hastened to my wardrobe and found almost all my clothes tossed about and torn to pieces.

My servant was perfectly right in his opinion of my cloak's madness. With my own eyes I saw it falling upon a fine full-dress suit, which it shook and tossed in the most unmerciful manner. Thinking this a timely moment to teach Jack a lesson, I said, "You will do well to observe the energy and thoroughness of the shaking the cloak gives the garments that otherwise would long have gone without a proper shaking."

About the beginning of his present Majesty's reign, some family business matters took me to the Isle of Thanet. While there, when the weather was fine, I found great enjoyment in and much benefit from my morning walks. After a number of these excursions, one day I saw an object upon a lofty hill about three miles distant. Being curious, I lengthened my usual walk and found it to be an ancient ruined temple of great beauty. On the eastern side were the remains of a tower nearly forty feet high. I examined the tower very carefully, thinking that, if I could reach its top, I should have a fine view of the surrounding country.

At last, by means of the ivy that grew in great abundance about it, I mounted the tower, but, I assure you, not without much difficulty and great danger. All of the top I found covered with ivy, except a large bowl-shaped chasm in the very middle. The darkness and depth of this hole excited my curiosity. Perhaps it might lead to an underground passage that penetrated the surrounding hills! Having no line with which

214

to sound its depth, I resolved to drop a stone down and listen
to the echo as it struck the bottom—if bottom there was.

Having found a stone that suited me perfectly, I placed
myself over the hole, with one foot on each side of it, and then
leaned down to listen as I dropped my stone. Immediately I
heard a rustling below, and suddenly a monstrous eagle
thrust up its head opposite my face, and, rising with irresisti-

ble force, carried me away seated on its large shoulders! I instantly grasped the bird about its neck, which was large enough to fill my arms. The creature's wings, when extended, were ten yards from tip to tip.

As the bird rose smoothly and evenly, my seat was easy, and I greatly enjoyed the view below me. My eagle hovered a while over Margate, and was seen by a number of people. Many shots were taken at us, and one ball hit the heel of my shoe, but did me no injury. My wingéd steed, disliking the treatment from below as much as I, directed its course to Dover Cliff, where it alighted. I thought of dismounting, but was prevented by a sudden discharge of musketry from a party of marines who were at target practice on the beach. The bullets flew about my head and rattled on the feathers of the eagle like hailstones, but as far as I could see it received no injury. It instantly, and with good reason, ascended and flew over the sea toward Calais, but at so great a height that the Channel looked to me no broader than the Thames at London Bridge.

In about a quarter of an hour I saw we were over a thick wood in France, where my eagle descended abruptly, causing me to slip down to the back part of its head. It alighted on a large tree and raised its head suddenly, and I slid back to my seat as before; but I had no chance of dismounting from my monster steed without the danger of being killed by a fall. After resting a few minutes, it took wing and flew several times around the wood, screaming loud enough to be heard across the English Channel.

In a few minutes one of the same species arose out of the wood and flew directly towards us. It looked at me with marks of displeasure, and came very near to me, but, deciding that I was too small an object to deserve notice, it con-

216

tinued its flight beside its mate. After several turns above the wood, the pair directed their course to the southwest.

I soon observed that the bird I rode could not keep pace with the other, but inclined towards the earth on account of my weight. Its companion, seeing this, turned around and placed itself directly ahead of my bird so that it could rest beak and neck upon the stalwart tail of the other. This act of intelligence and sympathy afforded me much pleasure. Thus we proceeded until noon, when I saw the Rock of Gibraltar very plainly.

The day was fine, and the earth's surface appeared quite like a map where land, sea, lakes, rivers, mountains, and the like were plain to be seen. Having considerable knowledge of geography, I was at no loss to decide what part of the globe I was flying over.

After looking upon the scene stretched beneath me for some time and with great pleasure, I saw that my eagles were about to alight on the peak of Teneriffe. With a downright speed that was terrifying, they descended upon the very crest of the rock, but seeing no chance to escape if I dismounted, I decided to remain where I was. My eagles settled down as if much fatigued by their long flight and the added burden of a passenger. The heat of the sun soon caused them both to fall asleep, nor could I long resist a desire to do likewise.

But in the cool of the evening I was aroused from sleep by the eagle moving beneath me. I had been stretched full length upon that feathered couch, but I sat up immediately, taking a safer position for my somewhat hazardous journey, away we hastened in the direction of South America. The moon was shining brightly during the whole night and I had a fine view of all the islands in those seas.

217

The night was thick and hazy
When the "Piccadilly Daisy"
Carried down the crew and captain in the sea;
    And I think the water drowned 'em;
    For they never, never found 'em,
And I know they didn't come ashore with me.

    Oh! 'twas very sad and lonely
    When I found myself the only
Population on this cultivated shore;
    But I've made a little tavern
    In a rocky little cavern
And I sit and watch for people
    at the door.

    I spent no time in looking
    For a girl to do my cooking,
As I'm quite a clever hand at
    making stews;
    But I had that fellow Friday,
    Just to keep the tavern tidy,
And to put a Sunday polish on my shoes.

Robinson Crusoe's Story

BY CHARLES EDWARD CARRYL

Illustrated by Susanne Suba

    I have a little garden
    That I'm cultivating lard in,
As the things I eat are rather tough and dry;
    For I live on toasted lizards,
    Prickly pears, and parrot gizzards,
And I'm really very fond of beetle-pie.

The clothes I had were furry,
And it made me fret and worry
When I found the moths were eating off the hair;
And I had to scrape and sand 'em,
And I boiled 'em and I tanned 'em,
Till I got the fine morocco suit I wear.

I sometimes seek diversion
In a family excursion
With the few domestic animals you see;
And we take along a carrot
As refreshment for the parrot,
And a little can of jungleberry tea.

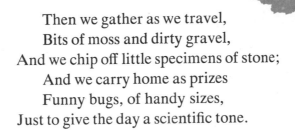

Then we gather as we travel,
Bits of moss and dirty gravel,
And we chip off little specimens of stone;
And we carry home as prizes
Funny bugs, of handy sizes,
Just to give the day a scientific tone.

If the roads are wet and muddy,
We remain at home and study,—
For the Goat is very clever at a sum,—
And the Dog, instead of fighting,
Studies ornamental writing,
While the Cat is taking lessons on the drum.

We retire at eleven,
And we rise again at seven;
And I wish to call attention, as I close,
To the fact that all the scholars
Are correct about their collars,
And particular in turning out their toes.

THERE was just one day of each week that worried Nasr-ed-Din Hodja. On six days he was as free as a butterfly. He could talk with his friends in the market place or ride his donkey to a nearby village. He could work in the vineyards or go hunting in the hills. He could lounge in the coffee house or sit in the sun in his own courtyard. There was nothing to hurry him to be at a certain place at a certain time to do a certain thing.

But Friday was different. It was much different. That was the day when all good Mohammedans went to their mosques. Because Nasr-ed-Din Hodja, years before, had attended the school for priests, he was expected each Friday to mount the pulpit of the mosque at a certain time and preach a sermon. That was all very well when he had something to say, but there were many Fridays when his mind was

Three Fridays

BY ALICE GEER KELSEY

Illustrated by Frank Dobias

as empty as that of his own little gray donkey. It was one thing to swap stories with the men in the coffee house and quite another to stand alone in the high pulpit and talk to a mosque full of people. The men, each squatting on his own prayer rug on the floor, looked up at him with such solemn faces. Then there was the fluttering in the balcony behind the lattices, which told him that the women were waiting too. Of course, the chanting, which came before the sermon, was not hard because all the men joined in that, bowing till they touched their foreheads to the floor in the Nemaz. But the sermon— that was hard.

One Friday he walked more slowly than ever through the

220

cobblestoned streets of Ak Shehir. He saw the veiled women slipping silently past him on their way to the latticed balcony of the mosque. He saw the men in their best clothes hurrying to the mosque to hear his sermon. But what 'sermon? He stopped at the mosque door to leave his shoes. He pattered with the other men across the soft thick rugs. But they could squat on the rugs, while he had to climb into the high pulpit.

Perhaps the beauty of the mosque would give him an idea. He looked up at the blues and reds and whites of the intricate tracery on the ceiling, but not a thought came. He looked at the rich yellows and reds of the mosaics on the walls, but there was no help there. He looked at the men's faces staring up at him. He heard the tittering in the latticed balcony where the veiled women sat. He must say something.

"Oh, people of Ak Shehir!" He leaned on the pulpit and eyed them squarely. "Do you know what I am about to say to you?"

"No!" boomed from the rugs where the men squatted.

"No!" floated down in soft whispers from the latticed balcony, whispers not meant for any ears beyond the balcony.

"You do not know?" said Nasr-ed-Din Hodja, shaking his head and looking from one face to another. "You are sure you do not know? Then what use would it be to talk to people who know nothing at all about this important subject. My words would be wasted on such ignorant people."

With that, the Hodja turned and climbed slowly down the pulpit steps. His eyes lowered, he walked with injured dignity through the crowds of men. He slipped on his shoes at the mosque door, and was out in the sunshine—free until next Friday.

That day came all too soon. The Hodja mingled with the crowds going to the mosque. His coarse, home-knit stockings

221

pattered across the deep colorful rugs. He climbed the steps to the high pulpit. He looked down at the sea of solemn faces. He heard the rustling behind the lattices of the balcony. He had hoped that this week he could think of a sermon, but the carvings of the doorway did not help him, nor the embroidered hangings of the pulpit, nor the pigeons fluttering and cooing at the window. Still, he must say something.

"Oh, people of Ak Shehir!" intoned the Hodja, gesturing with both hands. "Do you know what I am about to say to you?"

"Yes," boomed the men who remembered what had happened when they said "No" last week.

"Yes," echoed in soft whispers from the balcony.

"You know what I am going to say?" said the Hodja, shrugging first one shoulder and then the other. "You are sure you know what I am going to say? Then I need not say it. It would be a useless waste of my golden words if I told you something that you already knew."

The Hodja turned and again climbed down the pulpit steps. He picked his way with unhurried dignity among the men. He scuffed into his shoes and escaped into the sunshine. Another free week was ahead of him.

222

But the best of weeks end. The third Friday found him once more climbing the pulpit steps, with not a word worth saying in that solemn mosque. The ancient Arabic writing on the bright ceiling had no help for him. The flickering candles in the large round chandelier winked at him but said nothing. Even the big Koran in front of him might have had blank pages instead of its fine Arabic words and its illuminated borders. Men's faces looked up at him expectantly. Bright eyes peered through the lattices of the women's balcony. The time had come again when he must speak.

"Oh, people of Ak Shehir!" declaimed the Hodja as he groped helplessly for an idea. "Do you know what I am about to say to you?"

"No," came from those who were thinking of the last Friday.

"Yes," came from those who were thinking of the Friday before that.

"Some of you know and some of you do not know!" The Hodja rubbed his hands together and beamed down at the men. "How very fine! Now let those who know tell those who do not know!"

The Hodja was humming to himself as he came down from the pulpit, two steps at a time. He nodded and smiled as he threaded his way through the men. Some thought he bowed and smiled toward the latticed balcony, but others said the good Hodja would not have made so bold. He picked his own worn shoes from the rows and rows by the mosque door. The sunshine was warm and friendly. The birds were singing and there was the fragrance of hawthorn blossoms in the air.

The Hodja had not a worry in the world—not till another Friday should come around.

223

O L' PAUL was a great hunter, and as everyone knows, hunting is not much fun without a dog. But Paul traveled so fast when he hunted that the toughest dog was worn down to nothing but a puppy after a single day of trying to keep up with him. So one summer, when work was tolerable light, Ol' Paul set himself to solve this problem.

First he wrote his good friend P. T. Barnum to send him a bird dog, but was more than a little disappointed when the dog came to find that it couldn't fly. However, he spent all summer, spare times, teaching it to ride a bicycle. This was quite a chore, but he had considerable fun with the folks thereabouts, watching their eyes pop as he took great strides across the prairie with the dog on his bicycle, his long, silky ears flying in the wind, pedaling along behind. But when it came to hunting, the bicycle was useless in the brush and fallen timber, so finally Paul sent the dog back to Barnum, where he was quite an attraction.

Paul Goes Hunting

BY GLEN ROUNDS

Illustrated by Glen Rounds

About that time, one of the men came into camp with a pup he'd picked up somewhere. The little rascal wasn't much to look at; seemed to be half Dachshund and half Wolfhound, which gave him a high-behind appearance. Ol' Paul got an idea. He bought the dog and took over the care and feeding of it himself. He had a desk in his office that had a six-inch space under it, and under there was where he always fed the pup. When he filled the plate he'd shove it just exactly

224

halfway back. Naturally Skookum, as he was named, would run under to eat, with half his back and his hind quarters out in the room. Ol' Paul fed him nothing but sourdough pancakes and beef stew. As everybody knows, sourdough swells plenty, causing the pup to grow fast to keep up with it.

He couldn't help himself. As he was fed every ten minutes during the day and every seventeen minutes during the night, he spent practically all his time with his front quarters under the desk. Naturally they didn't have room to grow much, while his hind quarters were left free to grow as fast as they liked. In three weeks he had gained seventy-nine pounds and was still growing, and at the age of two months was full grown. He was still six inches high in front, but stood sixteen feet high behind. Naturally, with a build like that, he was always running downhill, even when he was going uphill. So no matter how far or how fast Ol' Paul traveled, Skookum followed him without the least trouble, coming in at night as fresh as a daisy.

One day Paul takes Skookum and his famous seventy-six barreled shotgun and rifle combined and goes hunting. He's hoping to get a Flu-flu bird. This was a rare bird that was always being heard but seldom seen by reliable people. According to reports it had a head like a turkey and a long bottle-green neck covered with scales the size and color of dimes. Its wings didn't match, the left being red or pink in color, and the right a dull black. It always flew backwards, never looking where it was going, but looking back towards where it had come from.

Ol' Paul and Skookum hunt for some time without seeing any signs of a Flu-flu bird. After a spell they come across a fresh moose trail, and start to follow that. But after a mile and three-quarters, the trail disappears completely. This

225

puzzles Paul more than somewhat, as he's the inventor of tracking and has never lost a trail before. After looking round a bit, they find a bear trail that looks mighty promising, so they start following that. First, however, he stops and polishes his sighting mirrors. You see, the seventy-six barrels are arranged to point in all directions, and he's rigged a complicated set of mirrors so that he can aim all seventy-six barrels at once. He's really loaded for bear.

But after another mile and three-quarters he loses the bear trail, and finds the moose trail again. This goes on for several hours, the trail changing every mile and three-quarters, until Paul gets so upset he's about ready to think he's seeing things. Luckily, he catches up with the end of the trail at the edge of a small swamp, and finds an animal of some kind mired down in the mud. He reaches down and gets it.

Although Ol' Paul has seen many strange things in his day, he'll be "teetotally jam switched if this isn't the beatinest yet." The beast has a head like a fox, except that its ears are much bigger and kind of floppy. Its shoulders and forelegs are those of a moose, but its hind legs stick up in the air, instead of down, and have the feet of a cinnamon bear. For trimming it has a long, hairless tail like a possum's, only much larger. It seems its habit was to walk a mile and three-quarters on the moose legs and then turn over and walk on the bear legs. This was so confusing to hunters that nobody had ever seen one before.

Ol' Paul looks at the thing for a while, and finally decides to name it a Bear-behind. Then he turns it loose, figuring he'll catch one nearer camp some time to show the men. But he never did.

THERE once lived a poor tailor who had a son called Aladdin, a careless, idle boy who would do nothing but play all day long in the streets with little idle boys like himself. This so grieved the father that he died; yet, in spite of his mother's tears and prayers, Aladdin did not mend his ways. One day, when he was playing in the streets as usual, a stranger asked him his age, and if he were not the son of Mustapha the tailor.

"I am, sir," replied Aladdin; "but he died a long while ago."

On this the stranger, who was a famous African magician, fell on his neck and kissed him, saying, "I am your uncle and I knew you from your likeness to my brother. Go to your mother and tell her I am coming."

Aladdin ran home and told his mother of his newly found uncle.

"Indeed, child," she said, "your father had a brother, but I always thought he was dead."

Aladdin and the Wonderful Lamp

EDITED BY

ANDREW LANG

Illustrated by John D. Batten

However, she prepared supper and made Aladdin seek his uncle, who came laden with wine and fruit. He presently knelt and kissed the place where Mustapha used to sit, bidding Aladdin's mother not to be surprised at not having seen him before, as he had been forty years out of the country.

He then turned to Aladdin and asked him his trade, at which the boy hung his head, while his mother burst into tears. On learning that Aladdin was idle and would learn no trade, he offered to take a shop for him and stock it with merchandise. Next day he bought Aladdin a fine suit of clothes and took him all over the city, showing him the sights, and brought him home at nightfall to his mother, who was overjoyed to see her son so fine.

Next day the magician led Aladdin into some beautiful gardens a long way outside the city gates. They sat down by a fountain, and the magician pulled a cake from his girdle, which he divided between them. They then journeyed onward till they almost reached the mountains. Aladdin was so tired that he begged to go back, but the magician beguiled him with pleasant stories and led him on in spite of himself.

At last they came to two mountains divided by a narrow valley. "We will go no farther," said the false uncle. "I will show you something wonderful; only do you gather up sticks while I kindle a fire."

When the fire was lit the magician threw on it a powder he had with him, at the same time saying some magical words. The earth trembled a little and opened in front of them, disclosing a square flat stone with a brass ring in the middle to raise it by. Aladdin tried to run away, but the magician caught him and gave him a blow that knocked him down.

"What have I done, uncle?" he said piteously.

Whereupon the magician said more kindly, "Fear nothing, but obey me. Beneath this stone lies a treasure which is to be yours, and no one else may touch it, so you must do exactly as I tell you."

At the word treasure, Aladdin forgot his fears and grasped the ring as he was told, saying the names of his father and grandfather. The stone came up quite easily and some steps appeared.

"Go down," said the magician. "At the foot of those steps you will find an open door leading into three large halls. Tuck up your gown and go through them without touching anything, or you will die instantly. These halls lead into a garden of fine fruit trees. Walk on till you come to a niche in a terrace where stands a lighted lamp. Pour out the oil it contains and bring it to me." He drew a ring from his finger and gave it to Aladdin, bidding him prosper.

Aladdin found everything as the magician had said, gathered some fruit off the trees and, having got the lamp, arrived at the mouth of the cave.

The magician cried out in a great hurry, "Make haste and give me the lamp." This Aladdin refused to do until he was out of the cave. The magician flew into a terrible passion, and throwing some more powder on the fire, he said something, and the stone rolled back into its place.

The magician left Persia forever, which plainly showed that he was no uncle of Aladdin's, but a cunning sorcerer who had read in his magic books of a wonderful lamp which would make him the most powerful man in the world. Though he alone knew where to find it, he could only receive it from the hand of another. He had picked out the foolish Aladdin for this purpose, intending to get the lamp and kill him afterward.

For two days Aladdin remained in the dark, crying and lamenting. At last he clasped his hands in prayer, and in so doing rubbed the ring, which the magician had forgotten to take from him.

Immediately an enormous and frightful genie rose out of the earth, saying, "What wouldst thou with me? I am the slave of the ring and will obey thee in all things."

Aladdin fearlessly replied, "Deliver me from this place," whereupon the earth opened, and he found himself outside. As soon as his eyes could bear the light he went home, but fainted on the threshold. When he came to himself he told his mother what had passed, and showed her the lamp and the fruits he had gathered in the garden, which were in reality precious stones. He then asked for some food.

"Alas, child," she said, "I have nothing in the house, but I have spun a little cotton and will go and sell it."

Aladdin bade her keep her cotton, for he would sell the lamp instead. As it was very dirty she began to rub it, that it might fetch a higher price. Instantly a hideous genie appeared and asked what she would have.

She fainted away, but Aladdin, snatching the lamp, said boldly, "Fetch me something to eat!"

The genie returned with a silver bowl, twelve silver plates containing rich meats, two silver cups, and a bottle of wine.

Aladdin's mother, when she came to herself, said, "Whence comes this splendid feast?"

"Ask not, but eat," replied Aladdin.

So they sat at breakfast till it was dinner time, and Aladdin told his mother about the lamp. She begged him to sell it and have nothing to do with genii.

"No," said Aladdin, "since chance has made us aware of its virtues, we will use it and the ring likewise, which I shall

231

always wear on my finger." When they had eaten all the genie had brought, Aladdin sold one of the silver plates, and so on till none were left. He then had recourse to the genie, who gave him another set of plates, and thus they lived for many years.

One day Aladdin heard an order from the sultan proclaiming that everyone was to stay at home and close his shutters while the princess, his daughter, went to and from the bath. Aladdin was seized by a desire to see her face, which was very difficult as she always went veiled. He hid himself behind the door of the bath and peeped through a chink.

The princess lifted her veil as she went in, and looked so beautiful that Aladdin fell in love with her at first sight. He went home so changed that his mother was frightened. He told her he loved the princess so deeply he could not live without her and meant to ask her in marriage of her father. His mother, on hearing this, burst out laughing, but Aladdin at last prevailed upon her to go before the sultan and carry his request. She fetched a napkin and laid in it the magic fruits from the enchanted garden, which sparkled and shone like the most beautiful jewels. She took these with her to please the sultan and set out, trusting in the lamp. The grand vizir and the lords of council had just gone in as she entered the hall and she placed herself in front of the sultan. He, however, took no notice of her. She went every day for a week and stood in the same place.

When the council broke up on the sixth day the sultan said to his vizir, "I see a certain woman in the audience chamber every day, carrying something in a napkin. Call her next time that I may find out what she wants."

Next day, at a sign from the vizir, she went up to the foot

of the throne and remained kneeling till the sultan said to her, "Rise, good woman, and tell me what you want."

She hesitated, so the sultan sent away all but the vizir and bade her speak freely, promising to forgive her beforehand for anything she might say. She then told him of her son's violent love for the princess.

"I prayed him to forget her," she said, "but in vain; he threatened to do some desperate deed if I refuse to go and ask Your Majesty for the hand of the princess. Now I pray you to forgive not me alone but my son Aladdin."

The sultan asked her kindly what she had in the napkin, whereupon she unfolded the jewels and presented them.

He was thunderstruck, and turning to the vizir, said, "What sayest thou? Ought I not to bestow the princess on one who values her at such a price?"

The vizir, who wanted her for his own son, begged the sultan to withhold her for three months, in the course of which he hoped his son would contrive to make him a richer present. The sultan granted this and told Aladdin's mother that, though he consented to the marriage, she must not appear before him again for three months.

Aladdin waited patiently for nearly three months, but after two had elapsed his mother, going into the city to buy oil, found everyone rejoicing and asked what was going on.

"Do you not know," was the answer, "that the son of the grand vizir is to marry the sultan's daughter tonight?"

Breathless, she ran and told Aladdin, who was overwhelmed at first, but presently bethought him of the lamp. He rubbed it, and the genie appeared, saying, "What is thy will?"

Aladdin replied, "The sultan, as thou knowest, has broken his promise to me, and the vizir's son is to have the princess.

233

My command is that tonight you bring hither the bride and
bridegroom."

"Master, I obey," said the genie.

Aladdin then went to his chamber where, sure enough at
midnight, the genie transported the bed containing the vizir's
son and the princess.

"Take this new-married man," Aladdin said, "and put him
outside in the cold and return at daybreak."

Whereupon the genie took the vizir's son out of bed, leaving Aladdin with the princess.

"Fear nothing," Aladdin said to her; "you are my wife,
promised to me by your unjust father, and no harm shall
come to you."

The princess was too frightened to speak and passed the
most miserable night of her life, while Aladdin lay down be-

234

side her and slept soundly. At the appointed hour the genie fetched in the shivering bridegroom, laid him in his place, and transported the bed back to the palace.

Presently the sultan came to wish his daughter good morning. The unhappy vizir's son jumped up and hid himself, while the princess would not say a word and was very sorrowful.

The sultan sent her mother to her, who said, "How comes it, child, that you will not speak to your father? What has happened?"

The princess sighed deeply, and at last told her mother how, during the night, the bed had been carried into some strange house, and what had passed there. Her mother did not believe her in the least but bade her rise and consider it an idle dream.

The following night exactly the same thing happened, and next morning, on the princess' refusing to speak, the sultan threatened to cut off her head. She then confessed all, bidding him ask the vizir's son if it were not so. The sultan told the vizir to ask his son, who owned the truth; adding that, dearly as he loved the princess, he had rather die than go through another such fearful night and that he wished to be separated from her. His wish was granted, and there was an end of feasting and rejoicing.

When the three months were over, Aladdin sent his mother to remind the sultan of his promise. She stood in the same place as before, and the sultan, who had forgotten Aladdin, at once remembered him and sent for her. On seeing her poverty the Sultan felt less inclined than ever to keep his word and asked the vizir's advice, who counseled him to set so high a value on the princess that no man living could come up to it.

235

The sultan then turned to Aladdin's mother, saying, "Good woman, a sultan must remember his promises and I will remember mine, but your son must first send me forty basins of gold brimful of jewels, carried by forty black slaves, led by as many white ones, splendidly dressed. Tell him that I await his answer."

The mother of Aladdin bowed low and went home, thinking all was lost. She gave Aladdin the message, adding, "He may wait long enough for your answer!"

"Not so long, mother, as you think," her son replied. "I would do a great deal more than that for the princess." He summoned the genie, and in a few moments the eighty slaves arrived and filled up the small house and garden.

Aladdin made them set out to the palace, two and two, followed by his mother. They were so richly dressed, with such splendid jewels in their girdles, that everyone crowded to see them and the basins of gold they carried on their heads.

They entered the palace and, after kneeling before the sultan, stood in a half-circle round the throne with their arms crossed, while Aladdin's mother presented them to the sultan.

He hesitated no longer but said, "Good woman, return and tell your son that I wait for him with open arms."

She lost no time in telling Aladdin, bidding him make haste. But Aladdin first called the genie.

"I want a scented bath," he said, "a richly embroidered habit, a horse surpassing the sultan's, and twenty slaves to attend me. Besides this I desire six slaves, beautifully dressed, to wait on my mother; and lastly, ten thousand pieces of gold in ten purses."

No sooner said than done. Aladdin mounted his horse and passed through the streets, the slaves strewing gold as they went. Those who had played with him in his childhood knew him not, he had grown so handsome.

236

When the sultan saw him, he came down from his throne, embraced him, and led him into a hall where a feast was spread, intending to marry him to the princess that very day. But Aladdin refused, saying, "I must build a palace fit for her," and took his leave.

Once home, he said to the genie, "Build me a palace of the finest marble, set with jasper, agate, and other precious stones. In the middle you shall build me a large hall with a dome, its four walls of massy gold and silver, each side having six windows whose lattices, all except one, which is to be left unfinished, must be set with diamonds and rubies. There must be stables and horses and grooms and slaves. Go and see about it!"

The palace was finished by next day, and the genie carried him there and showed him all his orders faithfully carried out, even to the laying of a velvet carpet from Aladdin's palace to the sultan's. Aladdin's mother then dressed herself carefully and walked to the palace with her slaves. The sultan sent musicians with trumpets and cymbals to meet them and the air resounded with music and cheers.

Aladdin's mother was taken to the princess, who saluted her and treated her with great honor. At night the princess said good-bye to her father and set out on the carpet for Aladdin's palace, with his mother at her side, and followed by the hundred slaves. She was charmed at the sight of Aladdin who ran to receive her.

"Princess," he said, "blame your beauty for my boldness if I have displeased you."

She told him that, having seen him, she willingly obeyed her father in this matter. After the wedding had taken place, Aladdin led her into the hall where a feast was spread, and she supped with him, after which they danced till midnight.

Next day Aladdin invited the sultan to see the palace. On

entering the hall with the four-and-twenty windows, with their rubies, diamonds, and emeralds, he cried, "It is a world's wonder! There is only one thing that surprises me. Was it by accident that one window was left unfinished?"

"No, sir, by design," returned Aladdin. "I wished Your Majesty to have the glory of finishing this palace."

The sultan was pleased and sent for the best jewelers in the city. He showed them the unfinished window and bade them fit it up like the others.

"Sir," replied their spokesman, "we cannot find jewels enough."

The sultan had his own fetched, which they soon used, but to no purpose, for in a month's time the work was not half done. Aladdin, knowing that their task was vain, bade them undo their work and carry the jewels back, and the genie finished the window at his command. The sultan was surprised to receive his jewels again and visited Aladdin, who showed him the window finished. The sultan embraced him, the envious vizir meanwhile hinting that it was the work of enchantment.

Aladdin had won the hearts of the people by his gentle bearing. He was made captain of the sultan's armies and won several battles for him, but remained modest and courteous as before and lived thus in peace and content for several years.

But far away in Africa the magician remembered Aladdin, and by his magic arts discovered that Aladdin, instead of perishing miserably in the cave, had escaped and had married a princess, with whom he was living in great honor and wealth. He knew that the poor tailor's son could only have accomplished this by means of the lamp and traveled night and day till he reached the capital of China, bent on

238

Aladdin's ruin. As he passed through the town he heard people talking everywhere about a marvelous palace.

"Forgive my ignorance," he asked, "what is this palace you speak of?"

"Have you not heard of Prince Aladdin's palace," was the reply, "the greatest wonder of the world? I will direct you if you have a mind to see it."

The magician thanked him who spoke and, having seen the palace, knew that it had been raised by the genie of the lamp and became half mad with rage. He determined to get hold of the lamp and again plunge Aladdin into the deepest poverty.

Unluckily, Aladdin had gone hunting for eight days, which gave the magician plenty of time. He bought a dozen copper lamps, put them into a basket, and went to the palace, crying, "New lamps for old!" followed by a jeering crowd.

The princess, sitting in the hall of four-and-twenty windows, sent a slave to find out what the noise was about.

The slave came back laughing, so the princess scolded her.

"Madam," replied the slave, "who can help laughing to see an old fool offering to exchange fine new lamps for old ones?"

Another slave, hearing this, said, "There is an old one on the cornice there which he can have."

Now this was the magic lamp, which Aladdin had left there, as he could not take it out hunting with him. The princess, not knowing its value, laughingly bade the slave take it and make the exchange. She went and said to the magician, "Give me a new lamp for this."

He snatched it and bade the slave take her choice, amid the jeers of the crowd. Little he cared, but left off crying his lamps, and went out of the city gates to a lonely place, where he remained till nightfall, when he pulled out the lamp and rubbed it. The genie appeared and at the magician's command carried him, together with the palace and the princess in it, to a lonely place in Africa.

Next morning the sultan looked out of the window toward Aladdin's palace and rubbed his eyes, for it was gone. He sent for the vizir and asked what had become of the palace. The vizir looked out, too, and was lost in astonishment. He again put it down to enchantment and this time the sultan believed him and sent thirty men on horseback to fetch Aladdin in chains. They met him riding home, bound him, and forced him to go with them on foot.

The people, however, who loved him, followed, armed, to see that he came to no harm. He was carried before the sultan, who ordered the executioner to cut off his head. The executioner made Aladdin kneel down, bandaged his eyes, and raised his scimitar to strike. At that instant the vizir, who saw that the crowd had forced their way into the courtyard and

240

were scaling the walls to rescue Aladdin, called to the executioner to stay his hand. The people, indeed, looked so threatening that the sultan gave way and ordered Aladdin to be unbound, and pardoned him in the sight of the crowd.

Aladdin now begged to know what he had done.

"False wretch!" said the sultan, "come hither," and showed him from the window the place where his palace had stood. Aladdin was so amazed that he could not say a word.

"Where is the palace and my daughter?" demanded the sultan. "For the first I am not so deeply concerned, but my daughter I must have and you must find her or lose your head."

Aladdin begged for forty days in which to find her, promising if he failed, to return and suffer death at the sultan's pleasure. His prayer was granted, and he went forth sadly from the sultan's presence. For three days he wandered about like a madman, asking everyone what had become of his palace, but they only laughed and pitied him.

He came to the banks of a river and knelt down to say his prayers before throwing himself in. In so doing he rubbed the magic ring he still wore. The genie he had seen in the cave appeared and asked his will.

"Save my life, genie," said Aladdin, "and bring my palace back."

"That is not in my power," said the genie. "I am only the slave of the ring, you must ask the slave of the lamp."

"Even so," said Aladdin, "but thou canst take me to the palace, and set me down under my dear wife's window." He at once found himself in Africa, under the window of the princess, where he fell asleep from sheer weariness.

He was awakened by the singing of the birds and his heart was lighter. He saw plainly that all his misfortunes were ow-ing to the loss of the lamp and vainly wondered who had robbed him of it.

That morning the princess rose earlier than she had since she had been carried into Africa by the magician, whose company she was forced to endure once a day. She, however, treated him so harshly that he dared not live there altogether. As she was dressing, one of her women looked out and saw Aladdin. The princess ran and opened the window, and at the noise she made Aladdin looked up. She called him to come to her, and great was their joy at seeing each other again.

After he had kissed her Aladdin said, "I beg of you, Princess, before we speak of anything else, for your own sake and mine, tell me what has become of an old lamp I left on the cornice in the hall of four-and-twenty windows, when I went hunting."

"Alas," she said, "I am the innocent cause of our sorrows," and told him of the exchange of the lamp.

"Now I know," cried Aladdin, "that we have to thank the African magician for this! Where is the lamp?"

"He carries it about with him," said the princess. "I know, for he pulled it out of his robe to show me. He wishes me to break my faith with you and marry him, saying that you were beheaded by my father's command. He is forever speaking ill of you, but I only reply by my tears. If I persist, I doubt not that he will use violence."

Aladdin comforted her and left her for a while. He changed clothes with the first person he met in the town and, having bought a certain powder, returned to the princess, who let him in by a little side door.

"Put on your most beautiful dress," he said to her, "and receive the magician with smiles, leading him to believe that you have forgotten me. Invite him to sup with you and say you wish to taste the wine of his country. He will go for some and while he is gone I will tell you what to do."

She listened carefully to Aladdin and, when he left her, arrayed herself gaily for the first time since she left China. She put on a girdle and headdress of diamonds, and seeing in a glass that she looked more beautiful than ever, received the magician, saying to his great amazement, "I have made up my mind that Aladdin is dead and that all my tears will not bring him back to me, so I am resolved to mourn no more and therefore invite you to sup with me. But I am tired of the wines of China and would fain taste those of Africa."

The magician flew to his cellar and the princess put the powder Aladdin had given her in her cup. When he returned she asked him to drink her health in the wine of Africa, handing him her cup in exchange for his as a sign she was reconciled to him.

Before drinking, the magician made her a speech in praise of her beauty, but the princess cut him short, saying, "Let me drink first, and you shall say what you will afterward." She set her cup to her lips while the magician drained his to the dregs and fell back lifeless.

The princess then opened the door to Aladdin and flung her arms round his neck, but Aladdin put her away, bidding her to leave him, as he had more to do. He then went to the dead magician, took the lamp out of his vest, and bade the genie carry the palace and all in it back to China. This was done, and the princess in her chamber only felt two slight shocks and little thought she was at home again.

The sultan, who was sitting in his closet, mourning for his lost daughter, happened to look up and rubbed his eyes, for there stood the palace as before! He hastened thither, and

Aladdin received him in the hall of the four-and-twenty windows, with the princess at his side. Aladdin told him what had happened and showed him the dead body of the magician, that he might believe. A ten days' feast was proclaimed, and it seemed as if Aladdin might now live the rest of his life in peace; but it was not to be.

The African magician had a younger brother, who was, if possible, more wicked and cunning than himself. He traveled to China to avenge his brother's death and went to visit a pious woman called Fatima, thinking she might be of use to him. He entered her cell and clapped a dagger to her breast, telling her to rise and do his bidding on pain of death. He changed clothes with her, colored his face like hers, put on her veil, and murdered her that she might tell no tales.

Then he went toward the palace of Aladdin, and all the people, thinking he was the holy woman, gathered round him, kissing his hands and begging his blessing. When he reached the palace there was such a noise round him that the princess bade her slave look out of the window and ask what was the matter. The slave said it was the holy woman, curing people of their ailments by her touch, whereupon the princess, who had long desired to see Fatima, sent for her.

On coming to the princess, the magician offered up a prayer for her health and prosperity. When he had done the princess made him sit by her and begged him to stay with her always. The false Fatima, who wished for nothing better, consented but kept his veil down for fear of discovery. The princess showed him the hall and asked him what he thought of it.

"It is truly beautiful," said the false Fatima. "In my mind it wants but one thing."

"And what is that?" said the princess.

244

"If only a roc's egg," replied he, "were hung up from the middle of this dome, it would be the wonder of the world."

After this the princess could think of nothing but a roc's egg, and when Aladdin returned from hunting he found her in a very ill humor. He begged to know what was amiss, but she told him that all her pleasure in the hall was spoilt for the want of a roc's egg hanging from the dome.

"If that is all," replied Aladdin, "you shall soon be happy."

He left her and rubbed the lamp, and when the genie appeared commanded him to bring a roc's egg. The genie gave such a loud and terrible shriek that the hall shook.

"Wretch," he cried, "is it not enough that I have done everything for you, but you must command me to bring my master and hang him up in the midst of this dome? You and your wife and your palace deserve to be burnt to ashes, but this request does not come from you but from the brother of the African magician whom you destroyed. He is now in your palace disguised as the holy woman—whom he murdered. He it was who put that wish into your wife's head. Take care of yourself, for he means to kill you." So saying the genie disappeared.

Aladdin went back to the princess, saying his head ached and requesting that the holy Fatima should be fetched to lay her hands on it. But when the magician came near, Aladdin, seizing his dagger, pierced him to the heart.

"What have you done?" cried the princess. "You have killed the holy woman!"

"Not so," replied Aladdin, "but a wicked magician," and told her how she had been deceived.

After this Aladdin and his wife lived in peace. He succeeded the sultan when he died, and reigned for many years, leaving behind him a long line of kings.

IN Midgard, in a northern Kingdom, a King reigned whose name was Alv; he was wise and good, and he had in his house a foster-son whose name was Sigurd.

Sigurd was fearless and strong; so fearless and so strong was he that he once captured a bear of the forest and drove him to the King's Hall. His mother's name was Hiordis. Once, before Sigurd was born, Alv and his father who was King before him went on an expedition across the sea and came into another country. While they were yet afar off they heard the din of a great battle. They came to the battlefield, but they found no living warriors on it, only heaps of slain. One warrior they marked: he was white-bearded and old and yet he seemed the noblest-looking man Alv or his father had ever looked on. His arms showed that he was a King amongst one of the bands of warriors.

Sigurd's Youth

BY PADRAIC COLUM

Illustrated by Enrico Arno

They went through the forest searching for survivors of the battle. And, hidden in a dell in the forest, they came upon two women. One was tall with blue, unflinching eyes and ruddy hair, but wearing the garb of a serving-maid. The other wore the rich dress of a Queen, but she was of low stature and her manner was covert and shrinking.

When Alv and his father drew near, the one who had on her the raiment of a Queen said, "Help us, lords, and protect us, and we will show you where a treasure is hidden. A great battle has been fought between the men of King Lygni and the men of King Sigmund, and the men of King Lygni have won the victory and have gone from the field. But King Sigmund is slain, and we who are of his household hid his treasure and we can show it to you."

"The noble warrior, white-haired and white-bearded, who lies yonder—is he King Sigmund?"

The woman answered, "Yes, lord, and I am his Queen."

"We have heard of King Sigmund," said Alv's father. "His fame and the fame of his race, the Volsungs, is over the wide world."

Alv said no word to either of the women, but his eyes stayed on the one who had on the garb of a serving-maid. She was on her knees, wrapping in a beast's skin two pieces of a broken sword.

"You will surely protect us, good lords," said she who had on the queenly dress.

"Yea, wife of King Sigmund, we will protect you and your serving-maid," said Alv's father, the old King.

Then the women took the warriors to a wild place on the seashore and they showed them where King Sigmund's treasure was hidden amongst the rocks: cups of gold and mighty arm-rings and jewelled collars. Prince Alv and his father put the treasure on the ship and brought the two women aboard. Then they sailed from that land.

That was before Sigurd, the foster-son of King Alv, was born.

Now the mother of Alv was wise and little of what she saw escaped her noting. She saw that of the two women that her son and her husband had brought into their kingdom, the one who wore the dress of the serving-maid had unflinching eyes and a high beauty, while the one who wore the queenly dress was shrinking and unstately. One night when all the women of the household was sitting round her, spinning wool by the light of torches in the hall, the Queen-mother said to the one who wore the queenly garb:

"Thou art good at rising in the morning. How dost thou know in the dark hours when it wears to dawn?"

The one clad in the queenly garb said, "When I was young I used to rise to milk the cows, and I waken ever since at the same hour."

The Queen-mother said to herself, "It is a strange country in which the royal maids rise to milk the cows."

Then she said to the one who wore the clothes of the serving-maid:

"How dost thou know in the dark hours when the dawn is coming?"

"My father," she said, "gave me the ring of gold that I wear, and always before it is time to rise I feel it grow cold on my finger."

"It is a strange country, truly," said the Queen-mother to herself, "in which the serving-maids wear rings of gold."

When all the others had left she spoke to the two women who had been brought into her country. To the one who wore the clothes of a serving-maid she said:

"Thou art the Queen."

Then the one who wore the queenly clothes said, "Thou art right, lady. She is the Queen, and I cannot any longer pretend to be other than I am."

Then the other woman spoke. Said she: "I am the Queen as thou hast said—the Queen of King Sigmund who was slain. Because a King sought for me I changed clothes with my serving-maid, my wish being to baffle those who might be sent to carry me away.

248

"Know that I am Hiordis, a King's daughter. Many men came to my father to ask for me in marriage, and of those that came there were two whom I heard much of: one was King Lygni and the other was King Sigmund of the race of the Volsungs. The King, my father, told me it was for me to choose between these two. Now King Sigmund was old, but he was the most famous warrior in the whole world, and I chose him rather than King Lygni.

"We were wed. But King Lygni did not lose desire of me, and in a while he came against King Sigmund's kingdom with a great army of men. We hid our treasure by the sea-shore, and I and my maid watched the battle from the borders of the forest. With the help of Gram, his wondrous sword, and his own great warrior strength, Sigmund was able to harry the great force that came against him. But suddenly he was stricken down. Then was the battle lost. Only King Lygni's men survived it, and they scattered to search for me and the treasure of the King.

"I came to where my lord lay on the field of battle, and he raised himself on his shield when I came, and he told me that death was very near him. A stranger had entered the battle at the time when it seemed that the men of King Lygni must draw away. With the spear that he held in his hand he struck at Sigmund's sword, and Gram, the wondrous sword, was broken in two pieces. Then did King Sigmund get his death-wound. 'It must be I shall die,' he said, 'for the spear against which my sword broke was Gungnir, Odin's spear. Only that spear could have shattered the sword that Odin gave my fathers. Now must I go to Valhalla, Odin's Hall of Heroes.'

" 'I weep,' I said, 'because I have no son who might call himself of the great race of the Volsungs.'

" 'For that you need not weep,' said Sigmund, 'a son will be born to you, my son and yours, and you shall name him Sigurd. Take now the broken pieces of my wondrous sword and give them to my son when he shall be of warrior age.'

"Then did Sigmund turn his face to the ground and the death-struggle came on him. Odin's Valkyrie took his spirit from the battle-field. And I lifted up the broken pieces of the sword, and with my serving-maid I went and hid in a deep dell in the forest. Then your husband and your son found us and they brought us to your kingdom where we have been kindly entreated, O Queen."

Such was the history that Hiordis, the wife of King Sigmund, told to the mother of Prince Alv.

Soon afterwards the child was born to her that was Sigmund's son. Sigurd she named him. And after Sigurd was born, the old King died and Prince Alv became King in his stead. He married Hiordis, she of the ruddy hair, the unflinching ways, and the high beauty, and he brought up her son Sigurd in his house as his foster-son.

250

Sigurd, the son of Sigmund, before he came to warrior's age, was known for his strength and his swiftness and for the fearlessness that shone round him like a glow. "Mighty was the race he sprang from, the Volsung race," men said, "but Sigurd will be as mighty as any that have gone before him." He built himself a hut in the forest that he might hunt wild beasts and live near to one who was to train him in many crafts.

This one was Regin, a maker of swords and a cunning man besides. It was said of Regin that he was an Enchanter and that he had been in the world for longer than the generations of men. No one remembered, nor no one's father remembered, when Regin had come into that country. He taught Sigurd the art of working in metals and he taught him, too, the lore of other days. But ever as he taught him he looked at Sigurd strangely, not as a man looks at his fellow, but as a lynx looks at a stronger beast.

One day Regin said to young Sigurd, "King Alv has thy father's treasure, men say, and yet he treats thee as if thou wert thrall-born."

Now Sigurd knew that Regin said this that he might anger him and thereafter use him to his own ends. He said, "King Alv is a wise and good King, and he would let me have riches if I had need of them."

"Thou dost go about as a foot-boy, and not as a King's son."

"Any day that it likes me I might have a horse to ride," Sigurd said.

"So thou dost say," said Regin, and he turned from Sigurd and went to blow the fire of his smithy.

Sigurd was made angry and he threw down the irons on which he was working and he ran to the horse-pastures by the great River. A herd of horses was there, gray and black and roan and chestnut, the best of the horses that King Alv possessed. As he came near to where the herd grazed he saw a stranger near, an ancient but robust man, wearing a strange cloak of blue and leaning on a staff to watch the horses. Sigurd, though young, had seen Kings in their halls, but this man had a bearing that was more lofty than any King's he had ever looked on.

"Thou art going to choose a horse for thyself," said the stranger to Sigurd.

"Yea, father," Sigurd said.

"Drive the herd first into the River," the stranger said.

Sigurd drove the horses into the wide River. Some were swept down by the current, others struggled back and clambered up the bank of the pastures. But one swam across the river, and throwing up his head neighed as for a victory.

Sigurd marked him; a gray horse he was, young and proud, with a great flowing mane. He went through the water and caught this horse, mounted him, and brought him back across the River.

"Thou hast done well," said the stranger. "Grani, whom thou has got, is of the breed of Sleipner, the horse of Odin."

"And I am of the race of the sons of Odin," cried Sigurd, his eyes wide and shining with the very light of the sun. "I am of the race of the sons of Odin, for my father was Sigmund, and his father was Volsung, and his father was Rerir, and his father was Sigi, who was the son of Odin."

The stranger, leaning on his staff, looked on the youth steadily. Only one of his eyes was to be seen, but that eye, Sigurd thought, might see through a stone. "All thou hast named," the stranger said, "were as swords of Odin to send men to Valhalla, Odin's Hall of Heroes. And of all that thou hast named there were none but were chosen by Odin's Valkyries for battles in Asgard."

Cried Sigurd, "Too much of what is brave and noble in the world is taken by Odin for his battles in Asgard."

The stranger leaned on his staff and his head was bowed. "What wouldst thou?" he said, and it did not seem to Sigurd that he spoke to him. "What wouldst thou? The leaves wither and fall off Ygdrassil, and the day of Ragnarök comes." Then he raised his head and spoke to Sigurd. "The time is near," he said, "when thou mayst possess thyself of the pieces of thy father's sword."

Then the man in the strange cloak of blue went climbing up the hill and Sigurd watched him pass away from his sight. He had held back Grani, his proud horse, but now he turned him and let him gallop along the River in a race that was as swift as the wind.

253

WHEN Uther Pendragon, King of England, died, the country for a long while stood in great danger, for every lord that was mighty gathered his forces, and many wished to be king. For King Uther's own son, Prince Arthur, who should have succeeded him, was but a child, and Merlin, the mighty magician, had hidden him away.

Now a strange thing had happened at Arthur's birth.

Some time before, Merlin had done Uther a great service, on condition that the King should grant him whatever he wished for. This the King swore a solemn oath to do. Then Merlin made him promise that when his child was born it should be delivered to Merlin to bring up as he chose, for this would be to the child's own great advantage. The King had given his promise so he was obliged to agree. Then Merlin said he knew a very true and faithful man, one of King Uther's lords, by name Sir Ector, who had large possessions in many parts of England and Wales, and that the child should be given to him to bring up.

The Marvel

of the Sword

BY MARY MACLEOD

Illustrated by Henry C. Pitz

On the night the baby was born, while it was still unchristened, King Uther commanded two knights and two ladies to take it, wrapped in a cloth of gold, and deliver it to a poor man whom they would find waiting at the postern gate of the Castle. This poor man was Merlin in disguise, although they did not know it. So the child was delivered unto Merlin and he carried him to Sir Ector, and made a holy man

254

christen him, and named him Arthur; and Sir Ector's wife cherished him as her own child.

Within two years King Uther fell sick of a great malady, and for three days and three nights he was speechless. All the Barons were in sorrow, and asked Merlin what was best to be done.

"There is no remedy," said Merlin, "God will have His Will. But look ye all, Barons, come before King Uther to-morrow, and God will make him speak."

So the next day Merlin and all the Barons came before the King, and Merlin said aloud to King Uther:

"Sir, after your days shall your son Arthur be King of this realm and all that belongs to it?"

Then Uther Pendragon turned and said in hearing of them all: "I give my son Arthur God's blessing and mine, and bid him pray for my soul, and righteously and honourably claim the crown, on forfeiture of my blessing."

And with that, King Uther died.

But Arthur was still only a baby, not two years old, and Merlin knew it would be no use yet to proclaim him King. For there were many powerful nobles in England in those days, who were all trying to get the kingdom for themselves, and perhaps they would kill the little Prince. So there was much strife and debate in the land for a long time.

When several years had passed, Merlin went to the Archbishop of Canterbury and counselled him to send for all the lords of the realm, and all the gentlemen of arms, that they should come to London at Christmas, and for this cause— that a miracle would show who should be rightly King of the realm. So all the lords and gentlemen made themselves ready, and came to London, and long before dawn on Christmas

255

Day they were all gathered in the great church of St. Paul's to pray.

When the first service was over, there was seen in the churchyard a large stone, foursquare, like marble, and in the midst of it was an anvil of steel a foot high. In this was stuck by the point a beautiful sword, with naked blade, and there were letters written in gold about the sword, which said thus:

Whoso pulleth this sword out of this stone
and anvil is rightly King of all England.

Then the people marvelled, and told it to the Archbishop.

"I command," said the Archbishop, "that you keep within the church, and pray unto God still; and that no man touch the sword till the service is over."

So when the prayers in church were over, all the lords went to behold the stone and the sword; and when they read the writing some of them—such as wished to be king—tried to pull the sword out of the anvil. But not one could make it stir.

256

"The man is not here, that shall achieve the sword," said the Archbishop, "but doubt not God will make him known. But let us provide ten knights, men of good fame, to keep guard over the sword."

So it was ordained, and proclamation was made that every one who wished might try to win the sword. And upon New Year's Day the Barons arranged to have a great tournament, in which all knights who would joust or tourney might take a part. This was ordained to keep together the Lords and Commons, for the Archbishop trusted that it would be made known who should win the sword.

On New Year's Day, after church, the Barons rode to the field, some to joust, and some to tourney, and so it happened that Sir Ecton, who had large estates near London, came also to the tournament; and with him rode Sir Kay, his son, with young Arthur, his foster brother.

As they rode, Sir Kay found he had lost his sword, for he had left it at his father's lodging, so he begged young Arthur to go and fetch it for him.

"That will I, gladly," said Arthur, and he rode fast away.

But when he came to the house, he found no one at home to give him the sword, for every one had gone to see the jousting. Then Arthur was angry and said to himself:

"I will ride to the churchyard, and take the sword with me that sticketh in the stone, for my brother, Sir Kay, shall not be without a sword this day."

When he came to the churchyard he alighted, and tied his horse to the stile, and went to the tent. But he found there no knights, who should have been guarding the sword, for they were all away at the joust. Seizing the sword by the handle he lightly and fiercely pulled it out of the stone, then took his horse and rode his way, till he came to Sir Kay his brother, to whom he delivered the sword.

As soon as Sir Kay saw it, he knew well it was the sword of the Stone, so he rode to his father Sir Ector, and said:

"Sir, lo, here is the sword of the Stone, wherefore I must be King of this land."

When Sir Ector saw the sword he turned back, and came to the church, and there they all three alighted and went into the church, and he made his son swear truly how he got the sword.

"By my brother Arthur," said Sir Kay, "for he brought it to me."

"How did you get this sword?" said Sir Ector to Arthur.

And the boy told him.

"Now," said Sir Ector, "I understand you must be King of this land."

"Wherefore I?" said Arthur. "And for what cause?"

"Sir," said Ector, "because God will have it so; for never man could draw out this sword but he that shall rightly be King. Now let me see whether you can put the sword there as it was, and pull it out again."

"There is no difficulty," said Arthur, and he put it back into the Stone.

Then Sir Ector tried to pull out the sword, and failed; and Sir Kay also pulled with all his might, but it would not move.

"Now you shall try," said Sir Ector to Arthur.

"I will, well," said Arthur, and pulled the sword out easily.

At this Sir Ector and Sir Kay knelt down on the ground.

"Alas," said Arthur, "mine own dear father and brother, why do you kneel to me?"

"Nay, nay, my lord Arthur, it is not so; I was never your

father, nor of your blood; but I know well you are of higher blood than I thought you were."

Then Sir Ector told him all, how he had taken him to bring up, and by whose command; and how he had received him from Merlin. And when he understood that Ector was not his father, Arthur was deeply grieved.

"Will you be good, gracious lord, when you are King?" asked the knight.

"If not, I should be to blame," said Arthur, "for you are the man in the world to whom I am the most beholden, and my good lady and mother your wife, who has fostered and kept me as well as her own children. And if ever it be God's will that I be King, as you say, you shall desire of me what I shall do, and I shall not fail you; God forbid I should fail you."

"Sir," said Sir Ector, "I will ask no more of you but that you will make my son, your foster brother Sir Kay, seneschal of all your lands."

"That shall be done," said Arthur, "and by my faith, never man but he shall have that office while he and I live."

Then they went to the Archbishop and told him how the sword was achieved, and by whom.

On Twelfth Day all the Barons came to the Stone in the churchyard, so that any one who wished might try to win the sword. But not one of them all could take it out, except Arthur. Many of them therefore were very angry, and said it was a great shame to them and to the country to be governed by a boy not of high blood, for as yet none of them knew that he was the son of King Uther Pendragon. So they agreed to delay the decision till Candlemas, which is the second day of February.

But when Candlemas came, and Arthur once more was the only one who could pull out the sword, they put it off till Easter; and when Easter came, and Arthur again prevailed in presence of them all, they put it off till the Feast of Pentecost.

Then by Merlin's advice the Archbishop summoned some of the best knights that were to be got—such knights as in his own day King Uther Pendragon had best loved, and trusted most—and these were appointed to attend young Arthur, and never to leave him night or day till the Feast of Pentecost.

When the great day came, all manner of men once more made the attempt, and once more not one of them all could prevail but Arthur. Before all the Lords and Commons there assembled he pulled out the sword, whereupon all the Commons cried out:

"We will have Arthur for our King! We will put him no more in delay, for we all see that it is God's will that he shall be our King, and he who holdeth against it, we will slay him."

And therewith they knelt down all at once, both rich and poor, and besought pardon of Arthur, because they had delayed him so long.

And Arthur forgave them, and took the sword in both his hands, and offered it on the altar where the Archbishop was and so he was made knight by the best man there.

After that, he was crowned at once, and there he swore to his Lords and Commons to be a true King, and to govern with true justice from thenceforth all the days of his life.

260

IN a town in Persia there dwelt two brothers, one named Cassim, the other Ali Baba. Cassim was married to a rich wife and lived in plenty, while Ali Baba had to maintain his wife and children by cutting wood in a neighboring forest and selling it in the town. One day, when Ali Baba was in the forest, he saw a troop of men on horseback, coming toward him in a cloud of dust. He was afraid they were robbers and climbed into a tree for safety. When they came up to him and dismounted, he counted forty of them. They unbridled their horses and tied them to trees.

The finest man among them, whom Ali Baba took to be their captain, went a little way among some bushes and said, "Open, Sesame!" so plainly that Ali Baba heard him. A door opened in the rocks and, having made the troop go in, he followed them and the door shut again of itself.

The Forty Thieves

EDITED BY ANDREW LANG

Illustrated by Louis Rhead

They stayed some time inside and Ali Baba, fearing they might come out and catch him, was forced to sit patiently in the tree. At last the door opened again and the forty thieves came out. As the captain went in last he came out first, and made them all pass by him; he then closed the door, saying, "Shut, Sesame!" Every man bridled his horse and mounted, the captain put himself at their head, and they returned as they came.

Then Ali Baba climbed down and went to the door concealed among the bushes and said, "Open, Sesame!" and it flew open. Ali Baba, who expected a dull, dismal place, was greatly surprised to find it large and well lighted, and hollowed by the hand of man in the form of a vault, which received the light from an opening in the ceiling. He saw rich bales of merchandise—silk stuffs, brocades, all piled together, gold and silver in heaps, and money in leather purses. He went in and the door shut behind him. He did not look at the silver but brought out as many bags of gold as he thought his asses, which were browsing outside, could carry, loaded them with the bags, and hid it all with fagots. Using the words, "Shut, Sesame!" he closed the door and went home.

Then he drove his asses into the yard, shut the gates, carried the moneybags to his wife and emptied them out before her. He bade her keep the secret and he would bury the gold.

"Let me first measure it," said his wife. "I will borrow a measure of someone while you dig the hole."

So she ran to the wife of Cassim and borrowed a measure. Knowing Ali Baba's poverty, the sister was curious to find out what sort of grain his wife wished to measure and artfully put some suet at the bottom of the measure. Ali Baba's wife went home and set the measure on the heap of gold and filled it and emptied it often, to her great content. She then carried it back to her sister, without noticing that a piece of gold was sticking to it.

Cassim's wife perceived it directly her back was turned. She grew very curious and said to Cassim when he came home, "Cassim, your brother is richer than you. He does not count his money, he measures it."

He begged her to explain this riddle, which she did by showing him the piece of money and telling him where she had found it. Then Cassim grew so envious that he could not sleep and went to his brother in the morning before sunrise.

"Ali Baba," he said, showing him the gold piece, "you pretend to be poor and yet you measure gold."

262

By this Ali Baba perceived that through his wife's folly Cassim and his wife knew his secret, so he confessed all and offered Cassim a share.

"That I expect," said Cassim, "but I must know where to find the treasure, otherwise I will discover all and you will lose all." Ali Baba, more out of kindness than fear, told him of the cave and the very words to use. Cassim left Ali Baba, meaning to be beforehand with him and get the treasure for himself. He rose early next morning and set out with ten mules loaded with great chests. He soon found the place and the door in the rock. He said, "Open, Sesame!" and the door opened and shut behind him.

He could have feasted his eyes all day on the treasures, but he now hastened to gather together as much of it as possible; but when he was ready to go he could not remember what to say for thinking of his great riches. Instead of "Sesame," he said, "Open, Barley!" and the door remained fast. He named several other sorts of grain, all but the right one, and the door still stuck fast. He was so frightened at the danger he was in that he had as much forgotten the word as if he had never heard it.

About noon the robbers returned to their cave and saw Cassim's mules roving about with great chests on their backs. This gave them the alarm. They drew their sabers, and went to the door, which opened on their captain's saying, "Open, Sesame!" Cassim, who had heard the trampling of their horses' feet, resolved to sell his life dearly, so when the door opened he leaped out and threw the captain down. In vain, however, for the robbers with their sabers soon killed him. On entering the cave they saw all the bags laid ready, and could not imagine how anyone had got in without knowing their secret. They cut Cassim's body into four quarters and nailed them up inside the cave, in order to frighten anyone who should venture in, and went away in search of more treasure.

As night drew on Cassim's wife grew very uneasy, ran to her brother-in-law and told him where her husband had gone. Ali Baba did his best to comfort her and set out to the forest in search of Cassim. The first thing he saw on entering the cave was his dead brother. Full of horror, he put the body on one of his asses and bags of gold on the other two and, covering all with fagots, returned home. He drove the two asses laden with gold into his own yard and led the other to Cassim's house. The door was opened by the slave Morgiana, whom he knew to be both brave and cunning.

Unloading the ass, he said to her, "This is the body of your master, who has been murdered, but whom we must bury as though he had died in his bed. I will speak with you again, but now tell your mistress I am come."

The wife of Cassim, on learning the fate of her husband, broke out into cries and tears, but Ali Baba offered to take her to live with him and his wife if she would promise to keep his counsel and leave everything to Morgiana; whereupon she agreed, and dried her eyes.

Morgiana, meanwhile, sought an apothecary and asked him for some lozenges. "My poor master," she said, "can neither eat nor speak and no one knows what his distemper is." She carried home the lozenges and returned next day weeping, and asked for an essence only given to those just about to die. Thus, in the evening, no one was surprised to hear the shrieks and cries of Cassim's wife and Morgiana, telling everyone that Cassim was dead.

The next day Morgiana went to an old cobbler near the gates of the town, who opened his stall early, put a piece of gold in his hand and bade him follow her with his needle and thread. Having bound his eyes with a handkerchief, she took him to the room where the body lay, pulled off the bandage and bade him sew the quarters together, after which she covered his eyes again and led him home.

Then they buried Cassim, and Morgiana, his slave, followed him to the grave, weeping and tearing her hair, while Cassim's wife stayed at home uttering lamentable cries. Next day she went to live with Ali Baba, who gave Cassim's shop to his eldest son.

The forty thieves, on their return to the cave, were much astonished to find Cassim's body gone as well as some of their money bags.

"We are certainly discovered," said the captain, "and shall be undone if we cannot find out who it is that knows our secret. Two men must have known it; we have killed one, we must now find the other. To this end one of you who is bold and artful must go into the city, dressed as a traveler, and discover whom we have killed and whether men talk of the strange manner of his death. If the messenger fails he must lose his life, lest we be betrayed."

One of the thieves started up and offered to do this and, after the rest had highly commended him for his bravery, he disguised himself and happened to enter the town at daybreak, just by Baba Mustapha's stall. The thief bade him good day, saying, "Honest man, how can you possibly see to stitch at your age?"

"Old as I am," replied the cobbler, "I have very good eyes, and you will believe me when I tell you that I sewed a dead body together in a place where I had less light than I have now."

The robber was overjoyed at his good fortune and, giving the cobbler a piece of gold, desired to be shown the house where he had stitched up the dead body. At first Mustapha refused, saying that he had been blindfolded. But when the robber gave him another piece of gold he began to think he might remember the turnings if blindfolded as before. This means succeeded. The robber partly led him and was partly guided by him right in front of Cassim's house, the door of which the robber marked with a piece of chalk.

Then, well pleased, he bade farewell to Baba Mustapha and returned to the forest. By and by Morgiana, going out, saw the mark the robber had made, quickly guessed that some mischief was brewing and, fetching a piece of white chalk, marked two or three doors on each side, without saying anything to her master or mistress.

The thief, meanwhile, told his comrades of his discovery. The captain thanked him and bade him show him the house he had marked. But when they came to it they saw that five or six of the houses were chalked in the same manner. The guide was so confounded that he knew not what answer to make, and when they returned to the cave he was at once beheaded for having failed. Another robber was dispatched and, having won over Baba Mustapha, marked the house in red chalk; but Morgiana being again too clever for them, the second messenger was put to death also.

The captain now resolved to go himself but, wiser than the others, he did not mark the house but looked at it so closely he could not fail to remember it. He returned and ordered his men to go into the neighboring villages and buy nineteen mules and thirty-eight leather jars, all empty, except one which was full of oil. The captain put one of his men, fully armed, into each, rubbing the outside of the jars with oil from the full vessel. Then the nineteen mules were loaded with thirty-seven robbers in jars and the jar of oil, and reached the town by dusk.

The captain stopped his mules in front of the house and

said to Ali Baba, who was sitting outside for coolness, "I have brought some oil from a distance to sell at tomorrow's market, but it is now so late that I know not where to pass the night, unless you will do me the favor to take me in."

Though Ali Baba had seen the captain of the robbers in the forest, he did not recognize him in the disguise of an oil merchant. He bade him welcome, opened his gates for the mules to enter, and went to Morgiana to bid her prepare a bed and supper for his guest. He brought the stranger into his hall, and after they had supped went again to speak to Morgiana in the kitchen, while the captain went into the yard under pretense of seeing after his mules but really to tell his men what to do.

Beginning at the first jar and ending at the last, he said to each man, "As soon as I throw some stones from the window of the chamber where I lie, cut the jars open with your knives and come out, and I will be with you in a thrice."

He returned to the house and Morgiana led him to his chamber. She then told Abdallah, her fellow slave, to set on the pot to make some broth for her master, who had gone to bed. Meanwhile her lamp went out and she had no more oil in the house.

"Do not be uneasy," said Abdallah, "go into the yard and take some out of one of those jars."

Morgiana thanked him for his advice, took the oil pot, and went into the yard. When she came to the first jar the robber inside said softly, "Is it time?"

Any other slave but Morgiana, on finding a man in the jar instead of the oil she wanted would have screamed and made a noise. But she, knowing the danger her master was in, bethought herself of a plan and answered quietly, "Not yet, but presently."

She went to all the jars, giving the same answer, till she came to the jar of oil. She now saw that her master, thinking to entertain an oil merchant, had let thirty-eight robbers into his house. She filled her oil pot, went back to the kitchen and, having lit her lamp, went again to the oil jar and filled a large kettle full of oil. When it boiled she went and poured enough oil into every jar to stifle and kill the robber inside. When this brave deed was done she went back to the kitchen, put out the fire and the lamp, and waited to see what would happen.

In a quarter of an hour the captain of the robbers awoke, got up and opened the window. As all seemed quiet he threw down some little pebbles which hit the jars. He listened and as none of his men seemed to stir, he grew uneasy and went down into the yard. On going to the first jar and saying, "Are you asleep?" he smelt the hot boiled oil and knew at once that his plot to murder Ali Baba and his household had been discovered. He found all the gang were dead and, missing the oil out of the last jar, became aware of the manner of their death. He then forced the lock of a door leading into a garden and, climbing over several walls, made his escape. Morgiana heard and saw all this and, rejoicing at her success, went to bed and fell asleep.

At daybreak Ali Baba arose and, seeing the oil jars there still, asked why the merchant had not gone with his mules. Morgiana bade him look in the first jar and see if there was any oil. Seeing a man, he started back in terror.

"Have no fear," said Morgiana, "the man cannot harm you; he is dead."

Ali Baba, when he had recovered somewhat from his astonishment, asked what had become of the merchant.

"Merchant!" said she, "he is no more a merchant than I am!" and she told him the whole story, assuring him that it

268

was a plot of the robbers of the forest, of whom only three were left, and that the white and red chalk marks had something to do with it. Ali Baba at once gave Morgiana her freedom, saying that he owed her his life. They then buried the bodies in Ali Baba's garden, while the mules were sold in the market by his slaves.

The captain returned to his lonely cave, which seemed frightful to him without his lost companions, and firmly resolved to avenge them by killing Ali Baba. He dressed himself carefully and went into the town, where he took lodgings at an inn. In the course of a great many journeys to the forest he carried away many rich stuffs and much fine linen, and set up a shop opposite that of Ali Baba's son. He called himself Cogia Hassan, and as he was both civil and well dressed he soon made friends with Ali Baba's son and through him with Ali Baba, whom he was continually asking to sup with him.

Ali Baba, wishing to return his kindness, invited him into his house and received him smiling, thanking him for his kindness to his son. When the merchant was about to take his leave Ali Baba stopped him, saying, "Where are you going, sir, in such haste? Will you not stay and sup with me?"

The merchant refused, saying that he had a reason and, on Ali Baba's asking him what that was, he replied, "It is, sir, that I can eat no victuals that have any salt in them."

"If that is all," said Ali Baba, "let me tell you there shall be no salt in either the meat or the bread that we eat tonight."

He went to give this order to Morgiana, who was much surprised. "Who is this man," she said, "who eats no salt with his meat?"

"He is an honest man, Morgiana," returned Ali Baba, "therefore do as I bid you."

270

But she could not withstand a desire to see this strange man, so she helped Abdallah carry up the dishes and saw in a moment that Cogia Hassan was the robber captain and carried a dagger under his garment. "I am not surprised," she said to herself, "that this wicked man who intends to kill my master will eat no salt with him, but I will hinder his plans."

She sent up the supper by Abdallah, while she made ready for one of the boldest acts that could be thought on. When the dessert had been served, Cogia Hassan was left alone with Ali Baba and his son, whom he thought to make drunk and then murder them.

Morgiana, meanwhile, put on a headdress like a dancing-girl's and clasped a girdle round her waist, from which hung a dagger with a silver hilt, and said to Abdallah, "Take your tabor, and let us go and divert our master and his guest."

Abdallah took his tabor and played before Morgiana until they came to the door, where Abdallah stopped playing and Morgiana made a low curtsy.

"Come in, Morgiana," said Ali Baba, "let Cogia Hassan see what you can do," and turning to his guest, he said, "She is my housekeeper."

Cogia Hassan was by no means pleased, for he feared that his chance of killing Ali Baba was gone for the present, but he pretended great eagerness to see Morgiana, and Abdallah began to play and Morgiana to dance. After she had performed several dances she drew her dagger and made passes with it, sometimes pointing it at her own breast, sometimes at her master's, as if it were part of the dance. Suddenly, out of breath, she snatched the tabor from Abdallah with her left hand and holding the dagger in her right, held out the tabor to her master. Ali Baba and his son put a piece of gold into it and Cogia Hassan, seeing that she was coming to him, pulled out his purse to make her a present, but while he was putting his hand into it Morgiana plunged the dagger into his heart.

"Unhappy girl!" cried Ali Baba and his son. "What have you done to ruin us?"

"It was to preserve you, master, not to ruin you," answered Morgiana. "See here," opening the false merchant's garment and showing the dagger, "see what an enemy you have entertained! Remember, he would eat no salt with you; what more would you have? Look at him! He is both the false oil merchant and the captain of the forty thieves."

Ali Baba was so grateful to Morgiana for thus saving his life that he offered her to his son in marriage, who readily consented; and a few days after, the wedding was celebrated with great splendor. At the end of a year Ali Baba, hearing nothing of the two remaining robbers, judged they were dead, and set out to the cave. The door opened on his saying, "Open, Sesame!" He went in and saw that nobody had been there since the captain left it. He brought away as much gold as he could carry and returned to town. He told his son the secret of the cave, which his son handed down in his turn, so the children and grandchildren of Ali Baba were rich to the end of their lives.

P. S.

IN preparing this volume, the editors have selected stories and excerpts from complete books, and in those cases where the text of a book is reprinted in its entirety, only a few of the many delightful illustrations from the original have been used. For the benefit of those who would like to read and enjoy the complete books, the following list is given.

Alice's Adventures in Wonderland, BY LEWIS CARROLL—A Mad Tea-Party, 43.

Arabian Nights, ANDREW LANG—Aladdin and the Wonderful Lamp, 228; The Forty Thieves, 261.

The Book of King Arthur and His Noble Knights, BY MARY MACLEOD—The Marvel of the Sword, 254.

The Children's Munchausen, JOHN MARTIN—The Travels of Baron Munchausen, 207.

Homer Price, BY ROBERT MCCLOSKEY—The Doughnuts, 161.

It's Perfectly True and Other Stories, PAUL LEYSSAC—The Emperor's New Clothes, 1; The Ugly Duckling, 132.

Just So Stories, BY RUDYARD KIPLING—The Elephant's Child, 99.

Many Moons, BY JAMES THURBER, 10.

Not Really, BY LESLEY FROST—The Drawbridge, 27.

Ol' Paul, The Mighty Logger, BY GLEN ROUNDS—Paul Goes Hunting, 224.

Once the Hodja, BY ALICE GEER KELSEY—Money From the Sky, 52; Three Fridays, 220.

Peabody's Old Greek Myths, JOSEPHINE PEABODY—Icarus and Daedalus, 109.

Pepper and Salt, BY HOWARD PYLE—Clever Peter and the Two Bottles, 32.

The Peterkin Papers, BY LUCRETIA P. HALE—About Elizabeth Eliza's Piano, 97.

Raffy and the Honkebeest, BY RITA KISSIN, 85.

Rootabaga Pigeons, BY CARL SANDBURG—The Huckabuck Family and How They Raised Pop Corn, 59.

Shen of the Sea, BY ARTHUR BOWIE CHRISMAN—Pies of the Princess, 173.

Some Merry Adventures of Robin Hood, BY HOWARD PYLE—The Shooting-Match at Nottingham Town, 199.

A Street of Little Shops, BY MARGERY BIANCO—Mr. A and Mr. P, 21.

This Way to Christmas, BY RUTH SAWYER—The Voyage of the Wee Red Cap, 112.

Tyll Ulenspiegel's Merry Pranks, BY M. JAGENDORF—Bake Monkeys and Owls and the Baker Growls, 196.

The Wind in the Willows, BY KENNETH GRAHAME—The River Bank, 144.

Winnie-the-Pooh, BY A. A. MILNE—Piglet Meets a Heffalump, 64.

The Wonder Clock, BY HOWARD PYLE—How Boots Befooled the King, 74.

Subject Index

276

Index

280

The Emperor's New Clothes The Drawbridge

Many Moons

Clever Peter and the Two Bottles Pirate Don Durk of Dowdee

Money From the Sky

Mr. A and Mr. P

Icarus and Daedalus

Raffy and the Honkebeest

How Boots Befooled the King

The Cyclops

The Elephant's Child

Sigurd's Youth

The Ugly Duckling Piglet Meets a Heffalump